It's another great book from CGP...

Whichever subject you're doing, it's really important to use spelling,
punctuation and grammar correctly in your writing.

Happily, this CGP book is bursting with questions to help you practise
all those vital skills until you've mastered every last one.

CGP — still the best! ☺

Our sole aim here at CGP is to produce the highest quality books —
carefully written, immaculately presented and dangerously close to being funny.

Then we work our socks off to get them out to you
— at the cheapest possible prices.

Contents

Section Four — Grammar: Tenses

Section Five — Writing Skills

Published by CGP

Editors:
Anna Hall
Heather McClelland
Anthony Muller

With thanks to Glenn Rogers and Nicola Woodfin for the proofreading.

ISBN: 978 1 84762 408 6

Clipart from Corel®
Printed by Elanders Ltd, Newcastle upon Tyne.

Based on the classic CGP style created by Richard Parsons.

Plurals

'Plural' just means 'more than one'. Unfortunately there's more than one way to make them. Sometimes you can just add '-s', but others are trickier — there are rules to remember. Eek...

Q1 Add '-s' or '-es' to the words in italics to make them **plural**:

a) The *bench*........ were piled so high that they nearly fell on Stewart.

b) We'll be in trouble when my sister sees we've eaten all her *sweet*........

c) She always rushes everywhere as if she's being chased by a pack of mad *dog*........

d) The police need *witness*........ for the accident outside the shop.

e) I haven't done my homework because the computer has lost all my *file*........

f) Why do two *bus*........ come at once when there haven't been any for an hour?

g) There are a lot of *fox*........ living in towns these days.

Q2 Write the **plural forms** of the words in italics on the dotted lines:

a) The *monkey* poked me in the *kidney*.   .... , ...

b) Their *jersey* got stuck in the *chimney*.   .... , ...

c) The *boy* found a way of mending the *toy*.   .... , ...

Q3 Circle the words below that have a **plural** that ends in '**-ies**':

baby	chimney	ruby	story	valley
subway	key	spray	sky	fly

Q4 There are some mistakes in the **plural endings** of some of the words in the following passage. **Underline** the mistakes and write the **correct plurals** in the box below:

My favourite animal is a donkey. One of the reasons I like donkies is that they have great long eares. Their favourite hobbys are eating and cooking — they take lots of meat and vegetablies, and make the most delicious meals. I used to keep my donkeys in fieldes, but ever since it rained cats and dogies last Tuesday, I have to keep them all in boxs. I don't think they like it much in there, but I've promised to give them all pet puppys if they behave.

Plurals

Making a plural from a word ending in 'o' isn't always as simple as just adding an '-s'. "O dear", I hear you cry. Don't worry — it isn't that bad. Have a go at these and you'll soon be flying...

Q5 Choose the correct word from the box to **complete** each sentence:

photos	sopranos	banjos	discos

a) Do you ever go to any school .... ?

b) They sold .... and other musical instruments.

c) Have you taken any .... today?

d) I sing alto, but Sally and Karen are ....

Q6 Some words ending in 'o', like 'potato', might need '-es' on the end to make the plural. **Underline** all of these types of plurals in the sentences below, then write their **singular forms** on the dotted lines:

a) Our heroes ate mangoes on the volcanoes. ....

b) The ships lost their cargoes when they were hit by torpedoes. ....

c) The heavenly echoes made the angels drop their haloes. ....

Q7 Work out the **plurals** of the words in the box, then use the plurals to fill in the **gaps** in the sentences below:

tomato	kilo	zoo	radio	studio	hero	potato	stereo

a) Any shop that sells televisions will probably

sell .... and .... too.

b) Some people think .... are cruel.

c) My dog weighs about six ....

d) My childhood .... were mostly athletes.

e) If I'm going to sell vegetables, I'll have to be able to

spell '...............................' and '...............................'.

f) The dance classes all take place in different ....

Plurals

Same story here — if the word ends in 'f' or 'fe' there are certain rules you have to follow. It may help if you just check that the word looks right once you've made it into a plural.

Q8 There are some **mistakes** with the plurals in the following story.
Underline the mistakes, and write the **correct** plurals in the box below:

The wifes in the village had begun putting their loafs of bread up on high shelfs because the local wolfs kept acting like thiefs and stealing them. These fierce animals frightened the calfs in the hills, which meant they kept running off the cliffes in panic. The loss of cattle was threatening the lifes of the chief's people because they were running out of meat. Something had to be done.

"We'll have to get the army of dwarves in," said the chief.

The dwarves sharpened their knifes, wrapped themselfs in thick scarves and made disguises out of leafs as they waited for the wolves. However, the wolves were too clever — they used the panicked calves to distract the dwarves, and then stole the loaves in the confusion.

Q9 Write down the **plural forms** of these words:

a) man ....

d) mouse ....

b) woman ....

e) tooth ....

c) child ....

f) goose ....

Q10 Draw lines to **match** each word type with the correct plural-making instruction:

a) ends in consonant + y

b) ends in f

c) ends in e

d) ends in fe

e) e.g. sheep or deer

f) ends in s, x, ch or sh

add s

add es

cut off f, add ves

cut off fe, add ves

cut off y, add ies

do nothing at all

the plural of sheep

4

Prefixes

Prefixes are letters that get fixed onto the beginning of a word and change its meaning. See if you can fix up some answers to the questions on this page...

Q1   Use the prefixes 'un-' or 'in-' to give each of these words their **opposite meaning**:

a) happy ....

b) active ....

c) visible ....

d) cover ....

e) dress ....

f) fair ....

Q2   Add the **correct prefix** from the box below to each of these words:

| il-   im-   ir- |

a) resistible ....

b) legible ....

c) possible ....

d) patient ....

e) mature ....

f) logical ....

Q3   Use each of the words in **Q2** to fill the gaps in these sentences:

a) It's going to be .... to finish all this work in an hour.

b) Doing things in this order is ....

c) I'm trying to diet, but that ice cream is just ....

d) "You're so ....," she snapped at the boys who were trying to put a worm down her neck.

e) Don't be so ....! She'll be here in a minute.

f) I can't read this — your writing is completely ....

Eat me! Eat me! I'm delicious...

Q4   Add the correct **prefixes** to give each of these words its **opposite** meaning:

a) please ....

b) necessary ....

c) moral ....

d) understood ....

e) agree ....

f) legal ....

g) discrete ....

h) responsible ....

4

Prefixes

Different prefixes do different things — learning what each of them does will help you work out the meaning of the new word. These questions should help you to get those meanings down...

Q5 Underline the **root words** in each of these longer words. Then, write down a **new word** using the **same root word**, but with a **different prefix**, on the dotted line:

a) disappear .... f) unable ....

b) reuse .... g) disorder ....

c) precook .... h) undo ....

d) replace .... i) preview ....

e) supermarket .... j) underarm ....

Q6 Add a **prefix** to each of the words in **italics** to complete the sentences below:

a) Abdul's singing made him an .... *national* superstar.

b) The weather .... *cast* says it will rain all day.

c) I always use the .... *wave* — it's much quicker than the oven.

d) David needed to .... *fresh* his memory by rereading this page.

e) My parents bought me a new .... *cycle* for my birthday.

f) The source of the gossip was .... *known*.

g) I have to .... *agree* with you — Cola Bottles are much better than Strawberry Laces.

Q7 Draw lines to **match** up each prefix with a suitable root word. Write on the dotted lines next to each root word what you think the meaning of your linked **prefix** is:

a) mid- | social | ....

b) de- | heat | ....

c) anti- | day | ....

d) mis- | brief | ....

e) non- | sense | ....

f) re- | understood | ....

g) sub- | marine | ....

Suffixes

If prefixes are the letters that you fix to the start of a word, then suffixes— you guessed it... Suffixes are the letters that fix onto the end of a word. They're a bit trickier though — they have an annoying habit of mucking around with the spelling of the words you add them to.

Q1 Circle the **correct spellings** of the words below:

a) curable / cureable   d) noticeing / noticing   g) argueable / arguable

b) videoing / videing   e) responseible / responsible   h) reversible / reverseible

c) exciteed / excited   f) shaking / shakeing   i) brakeing / braking

Q2 Complete the table below by correctly adding each **suffix** to the root words:

Root Word	-ed	-ing	-able
describe	....	....	....
squeeze	....	....	....
achieve	....	....	....
admire	....	....	....
manage	....	....	....
adore	....	....	....
believe	....	....	....

Q3 Add the correct **suffixes** to the **root words** in the sentences below:

a) She was *care*............ not to disturb anyone as she crept in.

b) At ten to four, everyone had gone home and the school was *peace*............ .

c) He *desperate*............ wanted to be allowed to go on the trip.

d) Finishing the race in such a short time was a tremendous *achieve*............ .

e) Don't throw that away — it could be *use*............ .

f) He was a good *advertise*............ for his school.

g) You must measure ingredients *accurate*............ or the recipe won't work.

Section One — Spelling

Suffixes

Adding suffixes to words ending in 'y' can be tricky. "Y is that?", I hear you ask — it's because you often have to replace the 'y' with other letters, that's Y. Give it a go on this page...

Q4   Add the suffixes '**-ible**' or '**-able**' to correctly complete the unfinished words below:

a) His behaviour is *incred*........

b) Your cheek is *unbeliev*........

c) Your writing is only just *leg*........

d) The whole essay was barely *read*........

e) It was *terr*........ to see him so ill.

f) We all felt utterly *miser*........

g) It's *poss*........ that I made a mistake.

h) He's a very *reli*....... chap.

i) Who's *respons*........ for this mess?

j) There are several *identifi*........ problems.

k) The meal was completely *ined*........

l) It was a thoroughly *enjoy*........ evening.

Q5   **Correct** the spelling of the words in **italics** below:

a) His habit of keeping skunks made him rather *unemploiable* ....

b) Her ambition was to start her own hamster-grooming *busyness* ....

c) He hated being reminded of his win in the *prettyest* .... baby contest.

d) Their neighbour often *plaied* .... his piano very loudly.

e) Peter *enjoied* .... dressing up when he was younger.

f) The dog wasn't allowed on the chair until her coat had *dryed* ....

g) We need someone *relyable* .... to do our homework for us.

h) Ellie decided she *fancyed* .... some chocolate.

Peter had never really grown out of dressing up...

Q6   Use the **examples** provided to help you **complete** the tables below:

Adjectives

happy	**happier**	**happiest**
lazy	laz........	laz........
flashy	flash........	flash........
heavy	heav........	heav........

Verbs

justify	**justifies**	**justified**
multiply	mutipl........	multipl........
qualify	qualif........	qualif........
hurry	hurr........	hurr........

Suffixes

Whenever you add a suffix to a root word, you need to have a think about whether you need to get rid of, **or** add, any letters. Have a root around for some answers to these questions...

Q7   Add the suffix '**-ing**' to each of the words in **brackets**.
Use the new word to **complete** the sentences below:

a)   "This parrot is quite ....," said the pirate. *(annoy)*

b)   Hannah is .... me with the answers to the questions. *(supply)*

c)   Everyone at the disco was .... away all evening. *(party)*

d)   I'm .... some bacon for us to have for breakfast. *(fry)*

e)   There's no point in .... it. *(deny)*

f)   Tom soon found that .... his brother wasn't a good idea. *(copy)*

g)   Liam thought about .... for the chef position. *(apply)*

h)   I'm .... to understand how you worked this out. *(try)*

Q8   Use the suffixes '**-ed**' and '**-ing**' to **complete** the table below:

Root Word	-ed	-ing
tag	....	....
bat	....	....
prefer	....	....
hum	....	....
prod	....	....
step	....	....
limit	....	....
jog	....	....
visit	....	....
commit	....	....

Suffixes

A couple more questions on suffixes here — think about whether or not you need to double a letter and also what to do about the 'e's. Hopefully you'll find them 'e's—y peasy. Ahem...

Q9 Circle the words in **italics** which are **spelt correctly**:

a) Alice was having an *upsetting / upseting* day because the new project she was *startting / starting* was very difficult.

b) Jack was *distractted / distracted* by *gazing / gazeing* out of the window.

c) I would have *prefered / preferred* chocolate, but Bill only *offered / offerred* me vanilla.

d) "That's the *crazyest / craziest* thing I've ever heard," *shouted / shoutted* Josh.

e) Stop *wasting / wasteing* my time — I am *exhaustted / exhausted* .

f) *Shuting / Shutting* my shop early meant I could get some *gardening / gardenning* done.

g) Jenny was *hopping / hoping* she would be able to go *runing / running* after work.

h) After she had *emptied / emptyed* the bins, Aisha *tried / tryed* to fix the tap.

i) *Stopping / Stoping* himself from shouting at his dad *proved / provved* very difficult.

j) Matt was feeling very *borred / bored* after he had *studyed / studied* for three hours.

Q10 Underline the words which are **incorrectly** spelt in each of these sentences. **Rewrite** the words **correctly** underneath:

You might need to double a letter with some suffixes...

a) His thumb just fited in the plughole, but then it was traped.

.... / ....

b) She was so excitted that she began hoping up and down on the spot.

.... / ....

c) They hopped to find homes for all the baby rabbits before the next lot arrivved.

.... / ....

d) When they saw the look on her face, they wishhed they'd stoped.

.... / ....

e) He fell when he sawwed off the branch he was siting on.

.... / ....

Comparing Things

There's comparatively little on this page to confuse you. Basically we're comparing two ways of comparing things with some nice questions about comparatives. My head is spinning...

Q1   Add the suffix '-er' to change these words into **comparatives**:

a) fast ....

d) big ....

b) heavy ....

e) happy ....

c) pretty ....

f) wet ....

Q2   Use '**more... than**' and the adjective in **brackets** to fill in the gaps in these sentences:

a) Chocolate is .... sprouts. (*delicious*)

b) Cities are usually .... villages. (*crowded*)

c) Learning grammar is .... watching paint dry. (*boring*)

Q3   Use '**less... than**' and the adjective in **brackets** to fill in the gaps in these sentences:

a) Kitchen chairs are .... armchairs. (*comfortable*)

b) The view downstairs is .... the one upstairs. (*beautiful*)

c) Winter is .... Autumn. (*colourful*)

d) David is .... Susan. (*intelligent*)

Q4   **Complete** these sentences by using the words in brackets to form **comparatives**. You need to **decide** whether to use '**more**', add the suffix '**-er**', or **change** the words in brackets **completely**:

a) Apples are .... than crisps. (*healthy*)

b) Max is .... in maths exams than science exams. (*successful*)

c) This year's fireworks were .... than last year's. (*fantastic*)

d) Jack is .... at baking than Jenny. (*good*)

e) I like my tea .... than Matt does. (*weak*)

f) I wish I could spend .... time at school. (*little*)

g) Running is .... than walking. (*quick*)

h) I am .... at spelling than my sister. (*bad*)

i) Sarah's shoes are .... than Richard's. (*new*)

j) Revising is .... than going to the cinema. (*fun*)

CGP - KS3 - SPAG The Workbook

Saying Something is the Most or Least

So you thought you were done with suffixes — sorry to disappoint, but you'll need to familiarise yourself with them again to make superlatives for these questions...

Q1   **Circle** the correct option in each of these sentences:

a)   My phone is the *most expensive / expensivest* thing I own.

b)   Princess Perfect is the *beautifullest / most beautiful* .

c)   The Christmas party was the *merryest / merriest* .

Tip: '-est' is a suffix, so you need to follow the same spelling rules as you do when you add other word endings.

d)   Motorways are usually the *widest / wideest* roads.

e)   Football is the *funnest / most fun* sport.

Q2   Use '**least**' and the adjective in **brackets** to fill the gaps in the sentences below:

a)   This necklace is the .... piece of jewellery I own. *(valuable)*

b)   Anchovies are the .... pizza topping. *(popular)*

c)   Adam is the .... cat I have ever met. *(talkative)*

d)   Billy's flat is the .... one in the building. *(peaceful)*

e)   Alice is the .... person I know. *(funny)*

Q3   Add the suffix '**-est**' to these words to change them into **superlatives**:

a)   high   ....   d)   thick   ....

b)   empty   ....   e)   dry   ....

c)   sad   ....   f)   safe   ....

Q4   **Complete** the table below:

Adjective	Comparative	Superlative
....	less	....
much/many	....	....
....	....	worst
....	better	....

Silent Letters

Silent letters are super stealthy — they're seen but not heard. This can make spelling words with silent letters tricky. Keep an eye out for them as you work through these questions...

Q1 Some of the words in this story have **silent letters**. **Underline** all the words with a silent 't', 'c' or 'h' and then copy them out into the correct boxes below:

It was the first day of the Christmas holidays and Mary was enjoying not being at school. She spent the morning watching her mum cooking. She liked to listen to her mum singing while she worked.

After her mum had finished, they spent an hour wrapping presents. They used scissors to cut the paper and then fastened the gifts with tape. Then they made some cards, which took ages. Mary drew a nativity scene for her dad and a picture of a castle for her brother. She sprayed perfume on them to make them scented and then put them in their envelopes.

Silent 't'	Silent 'c'	Silent 'h'

Q2 **Circle** the **correct spellings** of the words below:

a) nowledge / knowledge   e) fasinate / fascinate   i) neel / kneel

b) conscience / consience   f) sutle / subtle   j) onest / honest

c) dout / doubt   g) ghost / gost   k) wrong / rong

d) coud / could   h) anser / answer   l) thum / thumb

Q3 Write in the correct **silent** letters to **complete** the sentences below:

a) The ......night used his s......ord to kill the dragon.

b) I need to ta......k to someone about my de......t.

c) C......emistry is the hardest s......ience lesson.

d) Emma's father wa......ked her down the ai......le on her wedding day.

e) John wanted to make a si......n that wou......d show people where to go.

f) T......o of the explorers left the group to search for the lost tom......

g) The ......hole football team started lifting weights to develop their mus......les.

Vowel Sounds

Vowels are like parents — they can be stressed or unstressed. You can usually tell which by listening to how they sound. You might find these questions easier if you read them aloud...

Q1   Fill in the correct **vowels** in these words and then write each word in the correct box:

a) diff....rent

b) diction....ry

c) instrum....nt

d) origin....l

e) int....rest

f) int....rrupt

g) prim....ry

h) marv....llous

i) veget....ble

j) fright....n

k) natur....l

l) parli....ment

Unstressed 'a'	Unstressed 'e'

Q2   **Circle** the **unstressed** vowel sounds in each of these words:

a) carrot

b) totally

c) horizon

d) lantern

e) necessary

f) delivery

g) fattening

h) ridiculous

i) memory

j) central

k) government

l) alphabet

m) jewellery

n) doctor

o) factory

Q3   Use 'er' or 'ar' to fill in the gaps in the sentences below:

a) They said it was *volunt........y*, but I don't remember volunteering.

b) If the ball goes over the *bound........y*, you score a four.

c) She *desp........ately* wanted a part in the play.

d) He always felt like giggling in the *libr........y*.

e) I *gen........ally* prefer football to rugby.

f) I always get *sep........ated* from my friends because I don't pay enough attention.

Hard and Soft 'c' Sounds

Some of these questions are about hard 'c' sounds — they sound hard, but they're not really...
It's those soft 'c' sounds that are really tricky. Practise both types in these questions.

Q1 **Circle** the 'soft c' sounds and **underline** the 'hard c' sounds in the sentences below:

a) The chemist cuddled his cat in the middle of the cemetery.

b) Cairo and Canberra are capital cities on different continents.

c) A circle of clouds collected around the centre of the canyon.

d) Captain Clark is a character who keeps lots of cats.

Q2 **Circle** the words that begin with a 'soft c':

cymbal	car	coat	cycling	circus
care	ceiling	cub	carry	call
century	cot	cut	cement	cinder

Q3 **Circle** the **correct spellings** of the words below:

a) acseptable / acceptable

b) license / lisense

c) accidentally / acsidentally

d) mussle / muscle

e) pronunsciation / pronunciation

f) receive / reseive

g) experience / experiense

h) expensive / expencive

i) sensible / sencible

j) innoscence / innocence

Tip: When adding suffixes to a word ending with a 'soft c' and an e, you need to check whether you need to drop the 'e'.

Q4 Add the **suffixes** in **brackets** to each of these root words:

a) service (able) ....

b) service (ing) ....

c) fierce (ly) ....

d) fierce (est) ....

e) price (less) ....

f) spice (y) ....

g) pronounce (ed) ....

h) replace (ment) ....

i Before e Rule

The 'i before e' rule is a bit like your favourite film — you think you know it, but every time you see it you notice something different. Use these questions to really get to grips with it...

Q1 Use the **'i before e'** rule to complete these words:

a) dec___ve   d) rec___ver   g) d___sel   j) hyg___ne

b) ach___ve   e) c___ling   h) th___f   k) rel___f

c) p___ce   f) rec___pt   i) n___ghbour   l) w___ght

Q2 There are some **'i before e'** spelling mistakes in the passage below.
Underline the mistakes and then write the words **correctly** in the box below:

I beleive that the 'i before e' rule is the cheif of all spelling rules.
It has acheived such popularity that it is percieved as being flawless.
However, it is actually a decietful and mischievous rule because it has a few
exceptions. Despite this minor flaw, you shouldn't reject it as either ancient
or a useless counterfiet. It might be a bit wierd, but as long as you learn the
exceptions, it can be a very efficient spelling reminder.

Q3 Add the **suffixes** in **brackets** to each of these words.
Write the new words on the dotted lines:

a) vacancy (es) ....   c) policy (es) ....

b) fancy (ed) ....   d) juicy (est) ....

What can you learn about the **'i before e'** rule from your new words?

....

....

Q4 **Circle** the words that **don't obey** the 'i before e' rule:

freight	shield	diet	protein
beige	conceit	fierce	friend
brief	species	foreign	reign
fancied	sufficient	niece	seize

Name: date:

Commonly Misused Words

Here are some more words that often trip people up — but not literally, you'll be glad to hear...

Q1   **Circle** the **correct option** from each of the words in italics:

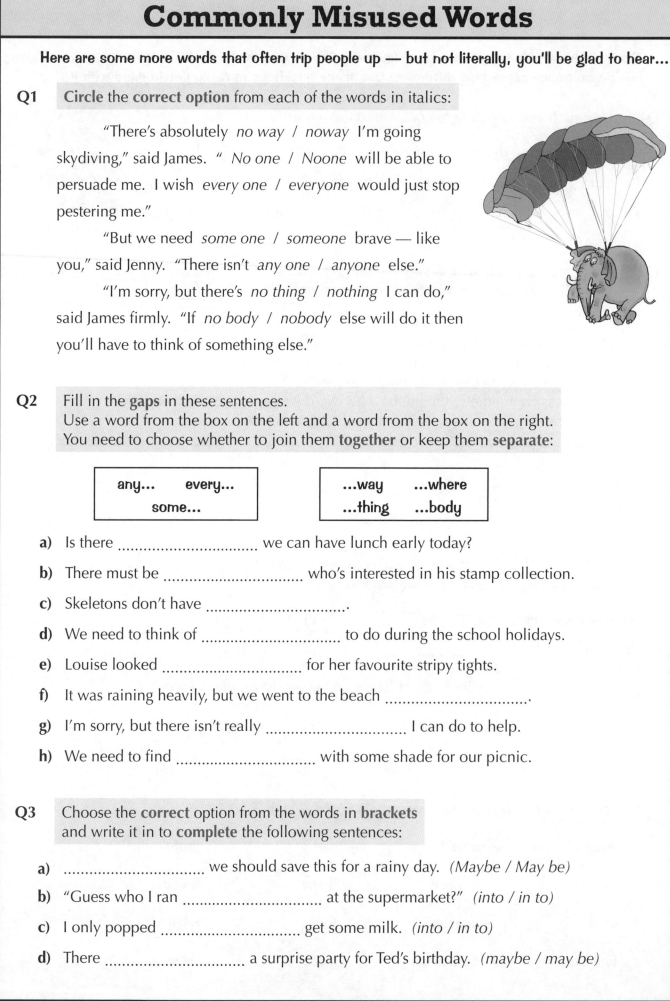

"There's absolutely *no way / noway* I'm going skydiving," said James. " *No one / Noone* will be able to persuade me. I wish *every one / everyone* would just stop pestering me."

"But we need *some one / someone* brave — like you," said Jenny. "There isn't *any one / anyone* else."

"I'm sorry, but there's *no thing / nothing* I can do," said James firmly. "If *no body / nobody* else will do it then you'll have to think of something else."

Q2   Fill in the **gaps** in these sentences.
Use a word from the box on the left and a word from the box on the right.
You need to choose whether to join them **together** or keep them **separate**:

any...   every...
some...

...way	...where
...thing	...body

a)   Is there .... we can have lunch early today?

b)   There must be .... who's interested in his stamp collection.

c)   Skeletons don't have ....

d)   We need to think of .... to do during the school holidays.

e)   Louise looked .... for her favourite stripy tights.

f)   It was raining heavily, but we went to the beach ....

g)   I'm sorry, but there isn't really .... I can do to help.

h)   We need to find .... with some shade for our picnic.

Q3   Choose the **correct** option from the words in **brackets** and write it in to **complete** the following sentences:

a)   .... we should save this for a rainy day. *(Maybe / May be)*

b)   "Guess who I ran .... at the supermarket?" *(into / in to)*

c)   I only popped .... get some milk. *(into / in to)*

d)   There .... a surprise party for Ted's birthday. *(maybe / may be)*

Commonly Misused Words

Yet more words on this page that can catch people out. It's those pesky words that sound the same but are spelt differently which cause problems. Try to get the hang of them here...

Q4   Circle the **correct option** in each of the sentences below:

a) There is *alot* / *a lot* of evidence to suggest that lollipops are better than ice creams.

b) *Thankyou* / *Thank you* for returning my fairy wings.

c) I don't have too many shoes; *infact,* / *in fact,* I don't have enough.

Q5   Use the letters 's' and 'c' to fill in the gaps **correctly** in the following sentences:

a) Mohammed *devi....ed* a way of teaching his rabbit to do his homework for him.

b) Aaron found his homework much easier after he had taken Charlotte's *advi....e*.

c) I'm going to be late for netball *practi....e*.

d) Tricia's taxi is *licen....ed* to carry four passengers.

e) The photo on my driving *licen....e* is so embarrassing.

f) I would *advi....e* you to stop insulting your boss if you want to keep your job.

g) Mr Hunt began to *practi....e* his Christmas carols in May.

Tip: Checking whether the word is a noun or a verb will help you work out how to spell it.

Q6   Circle whether each word below is a **verb** or an **adjective**, and then write a **sentence** on the dotted lines which contains the word used correctly:

a) **past**   *verb* / *adjective*   ....
....

b) **passed**   *verb* / *adjective*   ....
....

Q7   Choose the **correct** word from the brackets, and **complete** the following sentences:

a) It doesn't seem to have any .... on me. *(affect / effect)*

b) I'm sorry, we don't .... credit cards. *(accept / except)*

c) Playing more sport will definitely .... your health. *(affect / effect)*

d) Alan likes all sweets, ... orange-flavoured ones. *(accept / except)*

Commonly Misused Words

Deal with these words like people with annoying voices — focus on the meaning, not the sound.

Q8 **Match** each word below with its correct **function**. The first one has been done for you:

Hint: Adverbs modify when, where or how something happens.

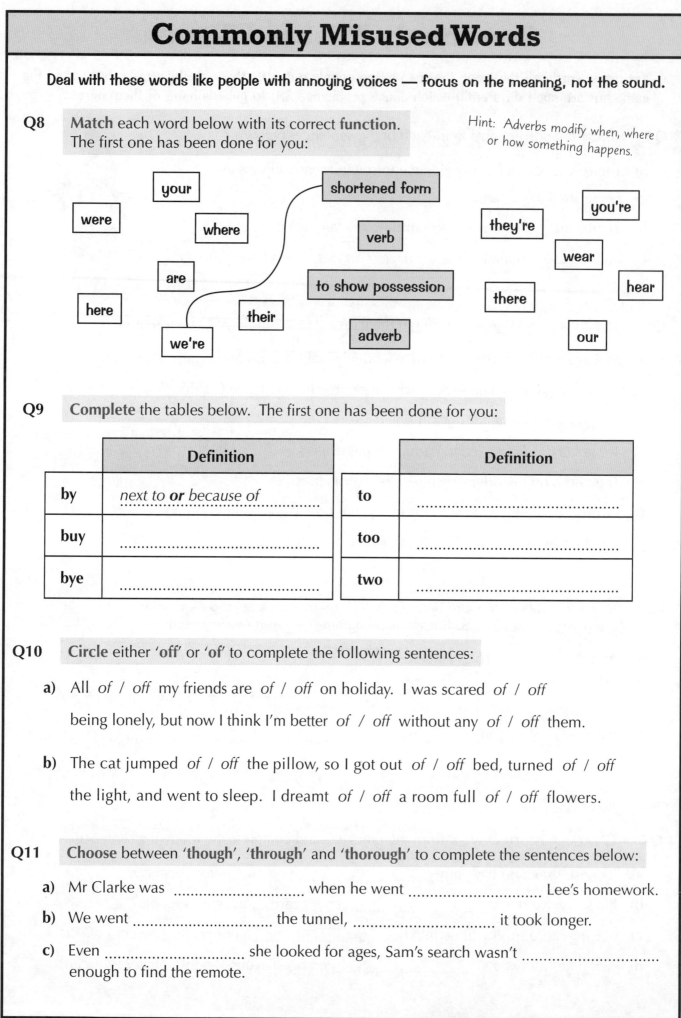

your

were

where

shortened form

verb

you're

they're

wear

are

to show possession

there

hear

here

their

we're

adverb

our

Q9 **Complete** the tables below. The first one has been done for you:

	Definition
by	*next to* **or** *because of* ....
buy	....
bye	....

	Definition
to	....
too	....
two	....

Q10 **Circle** either 'off' or 'of' to complete the following sentences:

a) All *of* / *off* my friends are *of* / *off* on holiday. I was scared *of* / *off* being lonely, but now I think I'm better *of* / *off* without any *of* / *off* them.

b) The cat jumped *of* / *off* the pillow, so I got out *of* / *off* bed, turned *of* / *off* the light, and went to sleep. I dreamt *of* / *off* a room full *of* / *off* flowers.

Q11 **Choose** between '**though**', '**through**' and '**thorough**' to complete the sentences below:

a) Mr Clarke was .... when he went .... Lee's homework.

b) We went .... the tunnel, ... it took longer.

c) Even .... she looked for ages, Sam's search wasn't .... enough to find the remote.

CGP- KS3- SPAG The Workbook

Commonly Misused Words

The good news is that this is the last page of questions on commonly misused words.
The bad news is that this page has the last pirate picture in the book...

Q12 **Underline** the spelling mistakes in the passage below and then write them **correctly** on the dotted lines underneath. **Pair** the **homophones** up with each other:

> It was a dark, cold night. The whether was horrible and the woulds around the house were wild and stormy. Olivia lay in bed and wished for some piece and quite.
> "I wish that rain wood stop," she said allowed.
> As the rain died down, Olivia started to wonder weather she could sneak downstairs for a peace of chocolate cake. She hadn't been aloud a slice at tea because she'd argued with her brother. He could be quiet a pain in the neck...

Eye've got an aye patch.

Even pirates confuse their words...

.... / ....

.... / .... / ....

.... / .... / ....

Q13 Use 'loose' or 'lose' to complete the following sentences:

a) One of my teeth is ...., but I don't want to .... it.

b) If any more frogs get ...., I may .... my job at the zoo.

Q14 **Underline** the **misused words** in each of these sentences. **Rewrite** the correct words on the dotted lines:

a) Can you pass me them crisps?   ....

b) Whose going to take me to hockey practice tonight?   ....

c) Who's stinky socks are those on the kitchen floor?   ....

Q15 Use the words in the box to **complete** the sentences below:

teach	learn	lend	borrow	brought	bought

a) You can .... this DVD if you .... me one in return.

b) I .... a packed lunch, but Ahmed .... his at the shops.

c) If I'm going to .... all this before the exam, someone will have to

.... me really well.

20

Mixed Questions

OK, we're mixing it up a bit on this page — have a go with this lovely selection of questions...

Q1 Write down the **plural forms** of these words:

a) box ....   e) part ....

b) agency ....   f) fish ....

c) foot ....   g) journey ....

d) half ....   h) leaf ....

Q2 Add the **prefixes** and **suffixes** in brackets to the following words:

a) *(sub)* conscious *(ly)* ....   e) *(re)* set *(ing)* ....

b) *(in)* accurate *(ly)* ....   f) *(un)* happy *(est)* ....

c) *(dis)* agree *(ment)* ....   g) *(pre)* define *(ed)* ....

d) *(mis)* dial *(ed)* ....   h) *(over)* stay *(ing)* ....

Q3 **Complete** the table below:

Adjective	Comparative	Superlative
....	smarter	....
....	sillier	....
fat	....	....
....	later	....
funny	....	....
....	....	bravest
....	further	....
....	madder	....

Section One — SpellingSection One — Spelling

Mixed Questions

Some more mixed questions here to help you avoid common spelling mix-ups...

Q4 Correct the **spelling** of the following words:

a) biskit ....

b) loveing ....

c) nifes ....

d) cryed ....

e) recieve ....

f) adjasent ....

g) sheild ....

h) embarass ....

i) managable ....

j) traveling ....

k) ryme ....

l) wellcome ....

Q5 Use the dotted lines to write down which **spelling rules** have been **forgotten** in each instance:

a) I wanted to write *snipping*, but I've written *sniping*. What have I forgotten to do?

....

....

b) I wanted to write *hoping*, but I've written *hopeing*. What have I forgotten to do?

....

....

c) I wanted to write *quiet*, but I've written *qiet*. What have I forgotten?

....

....

d) I wanted to write the plural of *dog*, but I've written *dog's*. Why's this wrong?

....

....

e) I wanted to write *neighbour*, but I've written *nieghbour*. What have I forgotten?

....

....

f) I wanted to write *pianos*, but I've written *pianoes*. What rule have I forgotten?

....

....

Mixed Questions

There are lots of different ways to make mistakes with spelling. Keep working through these questions to work out which spelling rules you need to concentrate on...

Q6   **Circle** the correct option from each of the groups below:

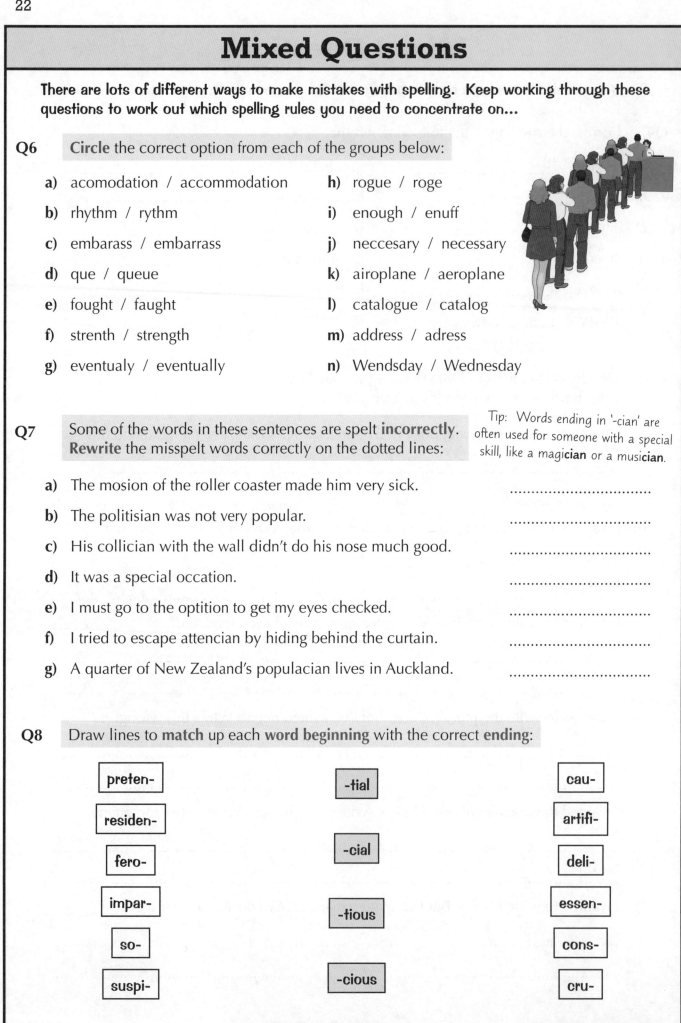

a) acomodation / accommodation

b) rhythm / rythm

c) embarass / embarrass

d) que / queue

e) fought / faught

f) strenth / strength

g) eventualy / eventually

h) rogue / roge

i) enough / enuff

j) neccesary / necessary

k) airoplane / aeroplane

l) catalogue / catalog

m) address / adress

n) Wendsday / Wednesday

Q7   Some of the words in these sentences are spelt **incorrectly**. **Rewrite** the misspelt words correctly on the dotted lines:

Tip: Words ending in '-cian' are often used for someone with a special skill, like a magi**cian** or a musi**cian**.

a) The mosion of the roller coaster made him very sick.   ....

b) The politisian was not very popular.   ....

c) His collician with the wall didn't do his nose much good.   ....

d) It was a special occation.   ....

e) I must go to the optition to get my eyes checked.   ....

f) I tried to escape attencian by hiding behind the curtain.   ....

g) A quarter of New Zealand's populacian lives in Auckland.   ....

Q8   Draw lines to **match** up each **word beginning** with the correct **ending**:

preten-		cau-
residen-	-tial	artifi-
fero-	-cial	deli-
impar-	-tious	essen-
so-		cons-
suspi-	-cious	cru-

Mixed Questions

This page has a few passages that contain lots of common spelling mistakes. See if you can find them all — it's a bit like spot the difference, but with words and more fun...

Q9 There are some **misspelt** words in the following passages. **Underline** the mistakes, and write the correctly spelt words on the dotted lines underneath.

Bob Angelo has been drawing skeches for years. He is probably famousest for his illustracian of a parade in the forground of Venice Cathedral. This pensil drawing highlites his incredable skill, and is currently on exibition at the British Gallery.

....

....

Occassionally, I visit the city square, where you can see all the impressive goverment buildinges. It's usually full of people, walking and chating. The atmosfere's brilliant. My favourite part is definitly the cathedral, witch is one of the grandest I've ever seen. The stained glass windows are especially beautifull. There's also a temprary coffee shop their, where you're garanteed to find delicious cakes and even more tastier hot chocolate. The nieghbouring chapel was built at a seperate time from the cathedral and is famous for haveing nuns buryied inside.

....

....

....

....

Yesterday the government was still feircely refusing to comment specificly on the matter. However, an offitial spokesman said: "The Prime Minister has no reason to beleive that the Secretary of State acted inapproprietely. Furthermore, he is an experiensed and consceintious member of the cabinet at the hight of his career." Other supporters of the Secretary have also confirmed there desire to keep him in office. Unfortunatly this issue is not likely to dissappear any time soon, and political advisors are warning that new strategys maybe nesessary if they are to gain enuff support for the Secretary to retain his job. In parliment, oppositian MPs are calling for explanatians, and asking qestions about the "outragious cover-up".

....

....

....

....

....

Punctuating Sentences

Keep practising your punctuation and it'll start to come naturally — like a duck to pancakes...

Q1 **Add question marks** or **full stops** to punctuate the following sentences correctly:

a) Tyrone asked if the cake was nice ......

b) Are you going to Shelley's party ......

c) Julian wished he was better at chess ......

d) Would you like ketchup or brown sauce ......

e) Adam wanted to know if the bread was mouldy ......

Q2 **Rewrite** the passage below so that the **capital letters** and **sentence endings** are correct:

My name is Beatrix. There aren't many famous people called Beatrix, but the Netherlands used to be ruled by queen beatrix. Her Reign lasted for over thirty Years, until she abdicated in april 2013.

Beatrix is also the name of a Famous writer that i love called Beatrix Potter! she was an english author who wrote about animals and the Countryside her most famous character is named peter rabbit — he's a Rabbit that gets into lots of Trouble.

However, my favourite story about rabbits is called 'Watership Down'. people often question if a Book all about rabbits would be enjoyable? Interestingly, everyone I know thinks it's amazing. Unfortunately, it's not by Beatrix potter.

....

....

....

....

....

....

....

....

....

....

....

....

....

....

Commas

Let's get to grips with those pesky commas — they're not as coma-inducing as they seem...

Q1   Add **commas** in the correct places in the sentences below:

a) I'd like to see Jane Phil and Peter after assembly.

b) Mary found it difficult to concentrate. Nevertheless she struggled on.

c) He's certain it's the right thing to do. However I'm not so sure.

d) Ice cream and chocolate sauce fish and chips and bangers and mash are all good combinations.

e) Metals are good conductors but non-metals are good insulators.

f) Peter's favourite colours are pink dark yellow and green.

g) There will be some big news this week so be sure to check the noticeboards.

h) We could go to bed or we could watch another film.

Q2   Add **commas** to separate the **extra information** in the sentences below:

a) My great grandmother who's ninety-six can remember the war.

b) Mr Green's car which is very new and shiny has got a big scratch on it.

c) Johnny one of my best friends is a very bad dancer.

d) Anaconda which is a very long word is extremely difficult to spell.

Q3   **Rewrite** the passage below so that the **commas** are in the correct places:

> Mr Hyde who is my teacher, brought his rabbit, into school yesterday. It has fluffy long white fur and is very, friendly. I don't really like rabbits but I loved Mr Hyde's rabbit. It was so cute, with its floppy ears big eyes, and long whiskers. Mr Hyde, even let me hold the rabbit for a bit. However I was worried that it might be dirty so I made sure I washed my hands afterwards.

....

....

....

....

....

....

....

Colons and Semicolons

Colons and semicolons are pretty tricky and people often make mistakes with them. If I've done my job properly these questions should help you avoid those common errors... (gulp)

Q1 Add **colons** in the correct places in the sentences below:

a) Jackie loves Christmas she always gets loads of presents.

b) Rosie was giggling Simon's joke was really funny.

c) Dogs are very lazy all they do is sleep all day.

d) There are two major problems with the act the jokes aren't funny, and we can't hear him.

Q2 Add **semicolons** in the correct places in the sentences below:

a) Ben has blue shoes Tony's shoes are red.

b) Shopping is very tiring it's probably more tiring than playing football.

c) I enjoy many hobbies: playing the violin, which my mum got me into playing chess, as it's a good mental challenge and football, because it's a good way to keep fit.

d) You are very good at playing the piano you must practise a lot.

Q3 Use the dotted line to explain the **difference** in meaning between the following two sentences:

a) The street emptied; the sheriff walked into town.

b) The street emptied: the sheriff walked into town.

....

....

....

Q4 **Choose** between a **colon** and a **semicolon** to complete the following sentences:

a) You'll need to bring .... a packed lunch, drinks, spare clothes and a sunhat.

b) We've had to cancel after-school hockey practice .... there's a shortage of light.

c) My parents had to go to a meeting with Mrs Lawrence, the Head of English .... Mr Kemp, my headteacher .... Mr Burton, my head of year .... and Jane Wood, the school counsellor.

Brackets and Dashes

Sorry — must dash, but I'll leave you to have a go at these brackets and dashes questions...

Q1   Add a **pair of brackets** to each of the sentences below:

a) It was too hot between 32 °C and 34 °C to do any exercise .

b) The twins Miles and Maisy were very loud .

c) You should read the FAQs frequently asked questions before contacting us .

d) My birthday 26th July is my favourite day of the year .

e) Pumas a type of big cat are very good hunters .

Q2   Add **dashes** in the correct places in the following sentences:

a) The swimmers were very calm until they saw the shark .

b) The model an enormous dinosaur skeleton was a big hit at the museum .

c) Johnny was not being sarcastic at all or was he ?

d) The Battle of Titan Hill was the most important battle
in November if not the whole war .

Q3   Choose either **brackets** or **dashes** to complete the following sentences:

a) Everyone was very relaxed .... until they noticed the huge spider.

b) My new neighbours .... Sue and Morris .... are very friendly.

c) ASAP .... as soon as possible .... is a very common acronym.

d) I always get lots of cards on February 14th .... Valentine's Day .... .

e) The room was completely empty .... or so we thought.

*Tip: Some of these sentences work with either brackets **or** dashes.*

Q4   Read the statements below and write '**true**' or '**false**' on the dotted lines:

a) Brackets are also known as parentheses.   ....

b) A sentence shouldn't make sense with
the information in brackets removed.   ....

c) Dashes should always be used in pairs.   ....

d) A single dash means you should pause when reading.   ....

e) Brackets should always be used in pairs.   ....

f) Brackets should only contain a maximum of two words.   ....

Hyphens

As we've seen, dashes are mega-exciting. Hyphens are a bit less fun, but they're still very important. Use these questions to learn when you should, and shouldn't, use them...

Q1 **Circle** the **correct option** in each of the following sentences:

a) My dad says he's having a *mid-life* / *mid life* crisis.

b) That wouldn't happen in *real-life* / *real life* .

c) I'm a *part-time* / *part time* employee.

d) My parrot is *twenty-seven* / *twenty seven* years old.

Q2 Add the **prefix** in brackets to each of these words:

Tip: Some words will need a hyphen.

a) *(ex)* husband ....

b) *(self)* confident ....

c) *(extra)* ordinary ....

d) *(re)* emerge ....

e) *(re)* read ....

f) *(under)* estimate ....

Q3 **Complete** the table below:

Word	This word needs a hyphen because...
re-cover	....
pro-British	....
co-own	....

Q4 Write down what each noun phrase **means**:

a) a man-eating shark ....

b) a man eating shark ....

c) a new-car salesman ....

d) a new car-salesman ....

e) five-year-old kittens ....

f) five year-old kittens ....

Apostrophes

Moving on to apostrophes now — these ones are used to show when words are missing a certain something... like letters. So keep an eye out for missing letters in these questions...

Q1 Add an **apostrophe** to the words in **italics** to complete these sentences:

a) I think *thats* the best thing that ever happened to me.

b) You *dont* all have to shout at once.

c) *Youre* the fastest worker I ever saw.

d) When they finish, *theyll* come over here.

e) I *cant* believe you remembered my birthday.

f) Do you know *whos* won the cup?

Q2 Use **apostrophes** to make **shortened forms** of the words in italics. Write your answers on the dotted lines:

a) You know you *cannot* ride a unicycle without falling off. ....

b) If Jo asks Simon, *he will* definitely take us. ....

c) *That is* all, folks! ....

d) *We are* going out to the cinema later. ....

e) It *does not* seem likely that he knows. ....

Q3 **Match** each **short form** below with its correct **long form**. The first one has been done for you:

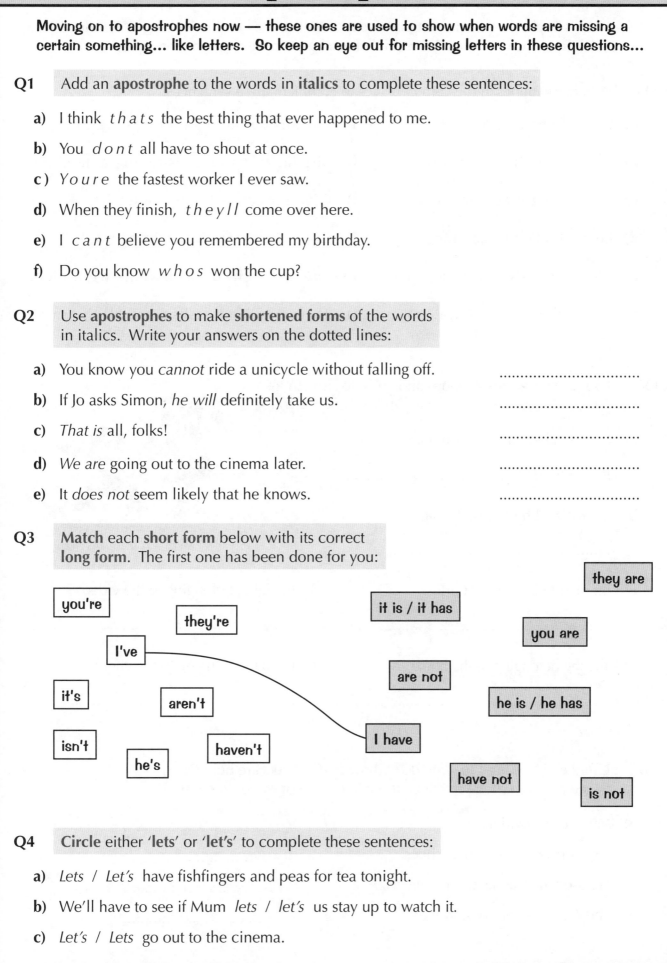

Q4 **Circle** either '**lets**' or '**let's**' to complete these sentences:

a) *Lets* / *Let's* have fishfingers and peas for tea tonight.

b) We'll have to see if Mum *lets* / *let's* us stay up to watch it.

c) *Let's* / *Lets* go out to the cinema.

Apostrophes

These apostrophes are a bit more possessive than the ones on the last page. But don't take any stick from them — show them who's boss by whizzing through these questions...

Q5 Add **apostrophes** in the correct places to complete these sentences:

a) Pass Mums bag over.

b) Bills football kit is filthy.

c) Ann is Elizabeths mum.

d) Leave Jacks things alone.

e) It's the ladies turn to go first.

f) That's the mices house.

g) Put all the babies pictures together.

h) Mrs Jacksons class is taking assembly.

i) Give me Janes homework.

j) Copy the work out of Toms book.

k) The other childrens parents were nice.

l) The womens dresses were all the same.

Q6 Use **possessive apostrophes** and an 's' to shorten the phrases below. The first one has been done for you:

a) the head belonging to the man

the man's head

b) the football belonging to Nat

There was some confusion over which was the man's head.

c) the scar belonging to Carlos

d) the leg belonging to the horse

e) the label belonging to the video

f) the hat belonging to the chef

Q7 Use the dotted lines to write down **how many** sisters are being talked about in each sentence. It might be **one** or **more than one**:

a) My sister's boyfriend is very nice.

b) She borrowed her sisters' shoes.

c) He used to steal his sisters' sweets.

d) They're my sister's best friends.

Apostrophes

Apostrophes are only little fellas, but they're super important. Keep going — just a few more...

Q8 Use **apostrophes** and extra letters to turn the words below into **possessives**.
Then use these possessives to fill in the **gaps** in the sentences below:

children	sheep	men	aircraft

a) I don't know why .... feet tend to be bigger than women's.

b) Our house is near the airport, so we can hear the .... engines all night.

c) The sponsored walk raised £300 for the .... playground.

d) The .... wool was very soft.

Q9 **Underline** the mistakes in the following sentences. Write
out the sentences **correctly** on the dotted lines underneath:

a) I've got my lunch, but I didnt pick your's up.

....

b) Jon said the book was his', but Sunita said it was her's.

....

c) I'm sure its hurt; it's got its wing hanging down.

....

d) Toms drawing is bigger, but I think mine's better.

....

e) They'll perform their's first, and then we'll do ours' when they're finished.

....

....

Q10 **Circle** either 'its' or 'it's' to complete these sentences:

a) *Its / It's* a shame that the school's hamster escaped.

b) *Its / It's* quite a rare breed, I think.

c) I think *its / it's* cage was broken.

d) *Its / It's* got a new one now.

e) Hopefully *its / it's* more secure than the last one.

f) The school says *its / it's* tested it thoroughly.

Speech Marks

OK, so speech marks can make punctuation pretty tricky, but it's important to get them right...

Q1   Add **speech marks** in the correct places to **complete** these sentences:

a) Have you got the sheepdog back yet ? asked Jeremy .

b) I'm sorry , I replied , I don't know the answer to that .

c) The children looked bored , so I asked, Would you like to go to the park ?

d) Stop pulling my hair ! screamed Alice .

e) Naz , if you don't give Adam's shoes back , he yelled , you'll regret it .

f) Where , she asked , in a moment of confusion , is my handbag ?

Q2   Add **speech marks** and **punctuation** correctly to the sentences below:

a) What would you like to do this weekend asked Melanie .

b) Please remind me said Tim that I need to be home for tea at six

c) I can't do it exclaimed Julia .

d) Personally added Steve I'm not really a big fan of vegetables

Q3   **Rewrite** the passage below with the correct punctuation:

As soon as Sophie went downstairs, her dad asked her if she was all right?

I'm fine said Sophie. It's just these horrible nightmares. She asked her dad if she looked tired?

I don't think so her dad replied, although he thought she looked exhausted.

Maybe I'll take a nap later — hopefully that will give me a bit of colour. mumbled Sophie as she left.

....

....

....

....

....

....

....

....

Speech Marks

The good news is you don't always need speech marks. Practise when to use them here...

Q4 **Rewrite** these sentences using **reported speech**:

A different kind of reported speech...

a) "What kind of cake shall I bake?" asked David.

....

b) "You should meet my mother," said Emily.

....

c) "I don't know the answer to that," replied Mr Clarkson.

....

Q5 **Rewrite** these sentences using **direct speech**:

a) Jamie told me that he didn't understand what I was saying.

....

b) My aunt asked for directions to the beach.

....

c) Ben's dad agreed to pick us up at nine o'clock.

....

Q6 Change the **adjectives** in brackets into **adverbs** and then combine them with the sentences to show **direct speech**. The first one has been done for you:

a) Elton John's a ruddy marvellous singer. *(passionate)*

"Elton John's a ruddy marvellous singer," he said passionately.

b) Do you think white stilettos are classy? *(sarcastic)*

....

c) Elvis is not dead. He's just resting. *(serious)*

....

d) My uncle used to be a rabbit. *(apologetic)*

....

e) Don't ever borrow my fishnets again. *(angry)*

....

Mixed Questions

Aha... A selection of mixed punctuation questions on this page. Time to get practising...

Q1 Read the passage below. Insert **full stops** and **capital letters** so that the passage is punctuated correctly. The first one has been done for you:

> ^L/ast summer, we went on holiday to spain we went in july, so the weather was beautiful my favourite thing about spain is the food i love the traditional spanish dishes like paella the best place to try paella is in madrid one weekend we went there to meet some friends — the knox family we ate at a restaurant called 'tavernita' i get on really well with the knox family, especially the two older boys (johnny and ollie) it's a shame that we only ever really see them at christmas

Q2 Choose between a **question** and an **exclamation mark** to complete these sentences:

a) How can you say that *? / !*

b) Watch out *? / !*

c) Is this legal *? / !*

d) Where is the emergency stop button *? / !*

e) Empty your pockets right now *? / !*

f) What is the meaning of this *? / !*

Q3 These sentences contain some comma mistakes. **Circle** the commas that are incorrect and **add** in commas where they're missing:

a) Let me know, if you want to come.

b) My elder sister who is a nurse has a lot of experience, in this area.

c) There are many new songs, several of which, are different from the old stuff.

d) I met a lot of interesting people some of whom, I really liked.

e) My computer, which is really old isn't working this morning.

f) She mentioned several things, that were bothering her.

Q4 Add **colons** in the correct places to **complete** these sentences:

a) "There's something else you don't know I hate rice pudding."

b) "I'll tell you how the other team beat us they cheated from start to finish."

c) You will need the following sugar, egg whites, cream, melted chocolate.

Mixed Questions

Surprise, surprise, more mixed questions. There's plenty to get your teeth into, so get cracking...

Q5   Read the statements below and write '**true**' or '**false**' on the dotted lines:

a)   You can use a semicolon to join two complete sentences. ....

b)   Semicolons should be used if the second sentence explains the first. ....

c)   Colons and semicolons do exactly the same job. ....

d)   A semicolon can be used to separate items in a list. ....

e)   Semicolons can be used to introduce a list. ....

f)   Semicolons are used to join sentences of equal importance. ....

Q6   Add a **pair of brackets** to each of the sentences below:

a)   People often use 'P.S.' postscript without knowing what it stands for .

b)   Dave my sister's boyfriend bought me a book for my birthday .

c)   The Declaration of Independence is celebrated on Independence Day 4th July .

d)   Dodos now extinct were large birds that couldn't fly .

Q7   **Rewrite** these sentences with **hyphens** in the correct places:

a)   The proBritish forces needed permission to reenter international waters.

....

....

b)   If you send me the forms, I'll resign them for the twenty second time.

....

....

c)   The eight year old girls are celebrating their eighth birthdays today.

....

....

Q8   Add **apostrophes** to correctly punctuate these sentences:

a)   Ive got Jamies trainers in my bag, but I cant give them back yet.

b)   Were on Marcuss team, but hes not as good as the other teams captains.

c)   Im not sure Id like the job shes just been offered.

Mixed Questions

Nearly there — just two more questions to help bring all those punctuation skills together...

Q9   Add **speech marks** and **punctuation** where needed to the sentences below:

a)   Mr Burns interrupted to ask if we had done all the questions

b)   Will you look after my bag whilst I go and order asked Heather

c)   You're so annoying exclaimed my sister

d)   I'm going to the shop said Aaron I need some chocolate

Q10   There are around **30 punctuation errors** in the passage below.
Rewrite the passage underneath, with the **correct** punctuation:

Last week, we went on a school trip to France we left on Wednesday morning the 27th and returned on Saturday evening the 30th.

have you got your lunch my mum asked on the morning of the trip. She told me to check the letter, from school, to see if I had forgotten anything. it said that i would need the following; a waterproof jacket spending money and some spare clothes.

My teacher Mr Jones organised the trip. he made sure it was cheap but the school said it's budget wouldnt cover flights We went by ferry instead which was fun — until — it got rough. Lots of people were ill: Jimmy, my exboyfriend, was sick on my shoes: as was Karen, the girl who sat in front of me: and ralph, whod had too many milkshakes.

....

....

....

....

....

....

....

....

....

....

....

....

....

Nouns

Nouns are words we use to name things, and there are lots of them — 'frown' is a noun, 'gown' is a noun, 'clown' is a noun, 'town' is a noun... I could go on forever.

Q1 Draw lines to **match** the following **definitions** to the correct **type of noun**:

a) These nouns are words that name a type of person or thing.

b) These nouns are the names of particular people and places (amongst other things).

c) These nouns are words for groups of things.

proper nouns

collective nouns

common nouns

Q2 Complete the table below by sorting the **words in the box** into the **correct columns**:

| February | pizza | cartoon | Robert | piano |
| horde of barbarians | bunch of grapes | Australia | bouquet of flowers |

Common Nouns	Proper Nouns	Collective Nouns
....	....	....
....	....	....
....	....	....

Q3 **Complete** this sentence: Proper nouns always start with a ....

Q4 Circle the **abstract** nouns in the words below:

money   honesty   freedom   desire   curtain   team

comfort   cloud   dream   wealth   forgiveness   gentleman

Q5 Complete the **crossword** below:

Across: Abstract Nouns

1) The opposite of sadness. (9)

2) The opposite of misfortune. (4)

3) Another word for gossip. (6)

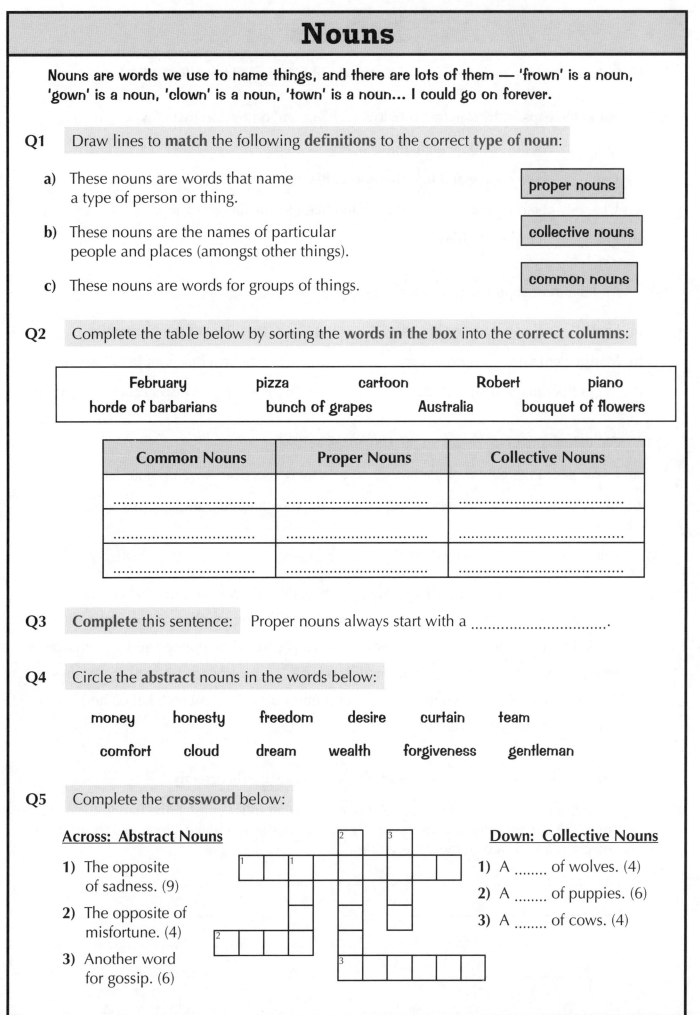

Down: Collective Nouns

1) A .... of wolves. (4)

2) A .... of puppies. (6)

3) A .... of cows. (4)

Articles

'A', 'an' and 'the' are really into art — that's why they're called 'art-icles', I think...

Q1 Fill in the **gaps** in the statements below with '**a**', '**an**' or '**the**' so that they are correct:

a) Use '......' or '......' for general things.

b) Use '......' before general things that sound like they begin with a consonant.

c) Use '......' before general things that sound like they begin with a vowel.

d) Use '......' for specific things.

Q2 Add the most appropriate **articles** to the sentences below:

a) I got .... new coat for my birthday.

b) Martin went on .... London Eye.

c) .... spider in the bath is stuck.

d) .... President of the Committee came.

e) .... time machine would be useful.

f) There was .... wasp's nest in .... roof.

Q3 Circle the correct '**a**' or '**an**' in the sentences below:

a) I saw *a / an* pig fly over the house.

b) Barcelona is *a / an* European city.

c) Jay was over *a / an* hour late.

d) The children built *a / an* igloo.

Q4 Add '**a**', '**an**' or '**the**' correctly to the passage below:

On .... way to school, Finley saw .... mayor of Stoatley land in a helicopter near .... centre of .... village. Its propellers made .... extremely loud noise as they whirled round. After .... few minutes, ... helicopter's door opened and .... mayor got out. He was wearing .... enormous top hat, ... pinstriped suit and .... orange bow tie. Suddenly, ... wind from .... propellers blew .... mayor's hat off and it landed right on top of Finley's head.

Q5 Rewrite the passage below so that all the **articles** are used **correctly**:

There is the theme park in Susie's town. It has an roller coaster, the haunted house, dodgems and the ghost train. The roller coaster is a highest in a country, and the ghost train is a extremely scary ride.

....

....

....

....

Pronouns

I love pronouns because they let me talk about me, me, me. But if I wanted to,
I could also use pronouns to talk about him, her, them, it and lots of other things.

Q1 Sort the words below into the **correct** boxes:

| we | she | his | ours | mine | theirs | it | its | yours | they |

Personal Pronouns	Possessive Pronouns

Q2 Rewrite these sentences by replacing the nouns in **italics** with suitable **pronouns**:

a) *Johnny* hates *football*. ➤ ....

b) *The hippos* scare *the lions*. ➤ ....

c) *Katy* invites *Kimberly*. ➤ ....

d) This is *your work*. ➤ ....

e) Those are *Tina's shoes*. ➤ ....

f) *Guy's* shirt is very nice. ➤ ....

Q3 Complete the **table** below:

Pronouns Doing an Action	Pronouns Being Acted On	Possessive Pronouns
I	....	....
....	him	....
....	....	yours

Q4 Circle the **correct** word in **italics** so that these sentences make sense:

a) The kids and *me / I* went to the swimming pool.

b) Give *me / I* the packet of sweets or the teddy bear gets it!

c) Frances, Kevin, Farah and *me / I* are all going to the theatre.

d) It's time you and *me / I* had a little chat.

Tip: If you're not sure, split the sentence into two and test whether you need 'I' or 'me'.

Pronouns

I pronoun-ce that this page will have more questions on pronouns...

Q5 The meaning of these sentences isn't 100% **clear**. For each sentence explain **why** it is **confusing** and **write out** a **clearer version**:

E.g. She had a sister and a dog; she was called Anna.

This is confusing because you don't know who is called Anna. It could mean the sister, the dog, or the 'she' at the beginning of the sentence. It would be clearer to write:

She had a sister and a dog; the dog was called Anna.

a) There was a fly on Jimmy's sandwich, so he crushed it.

....

....

....

b) The students asked the staff if they could help.

....

....

....

Q6 Add **'which'**, **'who'** or **'whom'** to these sentences so that they make sense:

a) I think the man .... cleans the windows is called Trevor.

b) Charlie doesn't know .... hat to buy.

c) To .... are you writing?

d) The clouds .... are floating over Millomswick are soft and fluffy.

e) The story is about a prince .... falls in love with a princess.

f) The person with .... I was speaking was very rude.

g) Karan's paintings, ... sell like hot cakes, are on display in the town hall.

Q7 Circle the **correct** word in **italics** so that these sentences make sense:

a) I don't know *who's / whose* dog won.

b) Where's the man *who's / whose* speaking?

c) *Who's / whose* that over there?

d) Does anyone know *who's / whose* jacket this is?

Verbs

Verbs are the most active word types — they just love to be doing things...

Q1 Circle the words below which are **verbs**:

take   drive   computer   go   already   laugh   are   happy   builder

Q2 Write the correct present tense forms of the verb '**to be**' on the dotted lines below:

a) I .... happy.

e) It .... annoying.

b) You .... tall.

f) We .... the best.

c) He .... handsome.

g) They .... nervous.

d) She .... silly.

Q3 Underline the **verbs** in the passage below that **do not agree** with their **subject**. Rewrite these verbs so that they **do agree** with their **subject** on the dotted lines below:

There are some cows that lives in the field just outside our house. They walks down our road every Tuesday, when the farmer move them from one field to the other. The neighbours always watches from their windows to see what are going on.

Normally, the cows hardly ever stops, but whenever they do, they always eats Mum's flowers. Once this starts to happen, nothing can get them to move, unless it rain. They does not like to get wet because the rain make their hooves go cold.

....

....

....

....

....

Q4 Write down whether the verbs in the sentences below are in the **present**, **past** or **future tense**:

a) The sun shone for six hours.   ....

b) Rachel daydreams a lot.   ....

c) Amir loves his deck chair.   ....

d) We will win the lottery one day.   ....

e) I forgot to turn the TV off.   ....

f) Boris will lose the election.   ....

Adjectives

Adjectives add a bit of colour to our sentences. They're great describing words — they mean I can describe myself as clever, beautiful, amazing and funny — and modest, of course...

Q1   **Complete** the following sentences, choosing the most suitable **adjectives** from the list below. You should only use each adjective **once**:

beneficial	tuneless	grotesque	competitive
invigorating	flavourless	athletic	rhythmical	manufactured
fattening	tense	harmonious	pointless

a) Some pupils think that homework is tedious, time-consuming and ....

b) However, teachers believe that homework is essential, educational and ....

c) Fast food is often described as greasy, ... and ....

d) I like horror movies because they are terrifying, ... and ....

e) My gran thinks that pop music is repetitive, ... and ....

f) Other people believe pop music is .... and ....

g) Active people enjoy sport because it's ...., ... and ....

Q2   **Rewrite** each of these sentences, adding **at least two adjectives** to make them more interesting:

a) The girl shouted.   ....

b) The car crashed.   ....

c) The boy cried.   ....

d) The baby slept.   ....

e) The alligator snapped.   ....

Q3   Add **commas** to these sentences where they are **needed**:

a) The monster was tall green and angry.

b) Chris eats smooth rich dark chocolate with crunchy salty crisps.

c) She's wearing an extra large bright pink woolly jumper.

d) I like quiet tidy clever housemates who appreciate good wholesome tasty home-made food.

e) Karin borrowed my extra long pale blue broken necklace.

Adverbs

Adverbs tell us how or when something happened — so they're a bit like news reporters...

Q1 Put the words below into the **correct box**:

quite   annoying   soon   readily   curly   happily   jolly   saintly   firstly

Adverbs	Adjectives

Q2 Underline the **adverb** in each sentence below. On the dotted line, write down whether it tells you **how**, **when** or **how often** the verb is done:

a) The birds flew gracefully. ....

b) Vampires never look in mirrors. ....

c) Today we're going to the cinema. ....

Q3 Turn the words in **brackets** into **adverbs** and add them to the sentences below. Write down an **adverb** that means the **opposite** on the dotted lines on the right:

a) We left the house .... (*quiet*) ....

b) They .... (*quick*) ran through the park. ....

c) The horse was behaving very .... (*strange*). ....

d) Janice filled in the form .... (*incorrect*) ....

e) Patreese .... (*occasion*) goes to the cinema. ....

Q4 Tick the boxes next to the words in italics which are **adverbial phrases**:

a) They completed the test *with great ease*. ☐

b) We ran out onto the playing field *as quickly as possible*. ☐

c) *Under the barrel*, there is a mouse. ☐

d) Wendy could see a house at the end *of the lonely street*. ☐

Tip: Not all adverbial phrases contain adverbs.

Q5 Write down whether the words **underlined** below are **adverbs** or **adjectives**:

a) <u>Most</u> cats chase mice. ....

b) The host family gave us a <u>friendly</u> welcome. ....

c) Lilly's tour around the city was <u>most</u> interesting. ....

Sentence Structure

All your favourite best-sellers started as a single sentence. Sentences are the building blocks of any written work. Write great sentences and the sky is the limit...

Q1 **Complete** the sentences a) to f) by writing in the **correct second halves** from i) to vi):

a) I asked her to phone me ....

b) Please let us know ....

Hint: Pay attention to the punctuation.

c) How would you like it ....

d) These are the things you'll need: ....

e) I don't know why he bought me a present — ....

f) Having read their postcard, ...

   i) if it happened to you?   iv) I wish I'd been there.

   ii) I didn't get him one.   v) when you plan to move in.

   iii) pyjamas, underwear and soap.   vi) as soon as she arrived.

Q2 **Rewrite** the rambling sentence below as a group of **shorter sentences**. You may need to **cut out** or **add words** to make the sentences work:

The unfortunate animal was eventually found in its hiding place, which was halfway up a tree at the bottom of the garden, and it was brought back down after a neighbour lent an extra long ladder which was only just long enough to reach the cat, which by now was absolutely terrified.

....

....

....

....

....

....

Q3 **Tick** the sentences which are **true**:

a) Long sentences are fine as long as your meaning is clear. ☐

b) Often a short sentence is clearer and more effective than a long one. ☐

c) The longer the sentence, the more impressed the examiner will be. ☐

d) If you get lost halfway through writing a sentence, your reader will get lost too. ☐

Phrases and Clauses

Phrases and clauses sound like a comedy double act, but they're actually grammatical terms.

Q1 Look at options **a)** - **f)** below. Write a '**P**' in the boxes next to those which are **phrases**:

a) Dad's trousers ☐

b) Tim wears purple trousers ☐

c) The trousers on the flag pole ☐

d) The terrible trousers ☐

e) I like trousers ☐

f) My other camouflage trousers ☐

Q2 In the table below, **tick** whether the words in bold are **phrases** or **clauses**:

Sentence	Phrase	Clause
The Martians invaded **on Tuesday morning**.		
I met a gerbil on the way to school.		
A clown came for tea at our house.		
Jude fell on the floor **with a loud crash**.		
During the beard festival, moustaches were banned.		

Q3 Draw a line to **match up** each clause in **Column A** with the correct clause in **Column B**. Then underline the **verbs** in each clause:

Column A

Whilst I was waiting for the bus,

Shouting as loud as I could,

Although I was feeling hungry,

Column B

I hated the thought of eating a horse.

Bob's car splashed me.

I tried desperately to get his attention.

Q4 Look at the **statements** below in relation to the clauses in **Q3**. Work out whether each statement **applies to** the clauses in **Column A** or the clauses in **Column B**:

a) They make sense on their own. ....

b) They are full sentences with a verb. ....

c) They are subordinate clauses. ....

d) They are main clauses. ....

Phrases and Clauses

This page talks a lot about where things are. It's great for ideas on where to hide during hide-and-seek, and it's pretty helpful for learning about prepositional phrases too...

Q5   Add your own **prepositional phrase** to each of the sentences below:

Tip: A prepositional phrase contains a preposition. Prepositions are words like 'in', 'over' or 'with'.

E.g. The fat, brown cat slept. ➡ **The fat, brown cat slept <u>on the bed</u>.**

a)   The yeti shouted ....

b)   A spaceship crashed ....

c)   Mike's mum laughed ....

d)   The alligator snapped ....

Q6   Look at the table below. Put a **tick** in each row to show whether the clause in **bold** is a **main** or **subordinate clause**:

Sentence	Main	Subordinate
I ate my breakfast before I went to bed.		
When I watch a film, I always eat a big bag of popcorn.		
Maisy couldn't play football **because she had lost her boots**.		
Our plumber, who is very tall, **hit his head on the ceiling**.		

Q7   Draw a line to **match up** each clause in column A with the correct clause in column B. Write on the dotted lines next to each sentence ending whether you have made a **complex** or **compound sentence**.

<u>Column A</u>

Tom went to the cinema

When I came home

I can juggle

<u>Column B</u>

I opened the post.   ....

whilst tap dancing.   ....

and saw a scary film.   ....

Q8   Add a **relative clause** using 'who' or 'which' to each sentence below:

a)   The frog was blue ....

b)   Henry wanted to see Daniel ....

c)   In America they play baseball ....

d)   Diana laughed at Kerry ....

Phrases and Clauses

Subordinate clauses sound tricky, but they're not that bad. Take a look for yourself...

Q9 Underline the **subordinate clauses** in the sentences below:

a) Keen to fly to Mars, Roy fired up the rocket ship.

b) Speaking from his heart, he showed how he really felt.

c) I do a sun dance around the kitchen whenever it rains.

d) The DVD, which I bought yesterday, was actually a VDD (Very Dusty Disc).

Get your 'clause' in.

Q10 Make each pair of sentences below into **one complex sentence**.
Underline the **subordinate clause** in your answer:

E.g. John was travelling by train. He was going to visit his grandma.
John was travelling by train <u>because he was going to visit his grandma</u>.

a) The dog growled at the man. It moved closer to him.

....

....

b) She was wearing her favourite dress. Sabrina chose to walk to the party.

....

....

c) I've run out of shampoo. I bought two bottles last week.

....

....

Q11 Rewrite each sentence in a **different order** by
moving the **subordinate clause** to a **new** position:

a) He wears his goggles while chopping onions.

....

b) As soon as the bell rang, the teachers ran out to their cars.

....

c) Despite meeting an elf, Beppe stayed calm.

....

d) You can't come to the party unless you're wearing pink.

....

Prepositions

If you ask someone to get something for you and they don't know where to look, you can help them find it using prepositions. Have a go at this page to test your knowledge...

Q1 Using **prepositions** correctly, describe **where** the following things are in the picture:

a) The picture frame is ....

b) The rat is ....

c) The lamp is ....

d) The teddy is ....

e) The girl is ....

f) The table is ....

Q2 Use the **prepositions** in the box below to fill in the gaps in this passage. You can only use each preposition once:

opposite	between	during	towards	aboard	across
around	beneath	amongst	against	within	along

To begin your tour of Garrenberg, you need to first head .... the city centre. The quickest way to get to the centre is to go via the marketplace. Walking through the marketplace can be hectic, and you need to watch out for pickpockets, who are often hidden .... the crowds.

Alternatively, you could take a longer walk and go around the outside of the city walls. .... 13 and 16 AD, a horde of barbarians launched an attack .... the city, which was responsible for much of the damage that is visible today.

If you have time, you should look .... the palace, and visit the royal chapel, where the royal tombs are buried right .... your feet. Walk .... the chapel square to find the palace café, which is open from 10 am to 4 pm .... the day, and from 6 pm to 9 pm in the evening.

.... the palace gates, the city's main shopping street is .... easy reach. Here you can buy postcards, souvenirs and local produce. Or you might like to climb .... a boat and enjoy a city cruise .... the River Mo.

Connectives

Broadband helps us humans feel connected, but sentences don't have access to the Internet. That's why we have connectives, which bring sentences together across the world...

Q1 Draw lines to match up the following **definitions** to the correct **sentence types**:

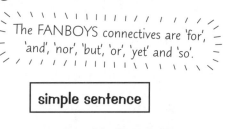

The FANBOYS connectives are 'for', 'and', 'nor', 'but', 'or', 'yet' and 'so'.

a) Two or more main clauses joined together with one of the FANBOYS connectives.

b) A sentence with two or more ideas joined by a connective which isn't one of the FANBOYS.

c) A sentence with one main clause.

$\boxed{\text{simple sentence}}$

$\boxed{\text{compound sentence}}$

$\boxed{\text{complex sentence}}$

Q2 **Underline** the **connectives** in each of these sentences:

a) While wearing a feather hat, my nose started to itch.

b) She remained calm until I ran up and down screaming "Emergency!"

c) It was dark in the cellar before we turned the lights on.

d) After Mark had gone to the shops, I raided the biscuit tin.

e) My dad has learnt to juggle since he joined the circus.

Q3 Underline any **connectives** in the sentences below. Write down whether each sentence is a **compound**, **complex** or **simple sentence** on the dotted line:

a) Rajwant runs on Wednesdays, and plays tennis on Mondays. ....

b) Rajwant runs because he likes to keep fit. ....

c) Rajwant runs in circles. ....

d) Rajwant runs to work if he gets up late. ....

e) Rajwant runs every day, yet he is still unfit. ....

Q4 **Add** the **connectives** in the box below correctly to sentences **a)** to **d)**:

although	while	so	since

a) .... the band was quite loud, Ben couldn't hear me.

b) Tanya went up the ladder .... Danny watched from below.

c) .... the maggots were on offer, Maggie didn't buy any.

d) The boy band 'Three Projection' came to town, ... I went to their concert.

Connectives

Connectives link sentences together. They can tell us when and why something happened, which is great when you want to tell your mate what happened in your favourite sitcom...

Q5   Using the **FANBOYS connectives**, complete the sentences below:

a)   We could either go to the gym .... we could play tennis.

b)   The music in the disco was awful, ... we still had fun.

c)   The chocolate cake was yummy, ... the blueberry muffins were delicious.

d)   We couldn't get tickets for the match, ... we watched it on TV instead.

Q6   Write **four sentences** using each of the **connectives** in the box once:

despite   whenever   although   whereas

a)   ....

   ....

b)   ....

   ....

c)   ....

   ....

d)   ....

   ....

Q7   Underline the **most suitable connectives** in the passage below:

Linda likes to spend her evenings curled up on the couch in front of the TV, *whereas / therefore* Roy likes to go to bed early.

Although / Meanwhile Roy likes a cooked breakfast in the morning, he always gets up too late and *however / therefore* has to have cereal instead. *However, / Therefore,* Linda is always up early and she takes the dog for a walk *until / unless* Roy finally gets out of bed. *During / Whilst* Roy is in the shower, Linda reads the newspaper, *despite / whereas* the dog goes back to bed.

Meanwhile / In spite of starting work earlier than Roy, Linda can leave the house later, *since / contrary to* she doesn't have to travel as far as he does. *Consequently / Despite* Roy sets off 15 minutes before Linda. *While / Although* Linda and Roy go out to work, the dog waits in her bed for the postman to arrive. The dog will often fall back to sleep. *Nevertheless, / Moreover,* she always hears the sound of the postman arriving.

Connectives

The connectives you choose to link your ideas give the reader a clue as to what's coming next — think of them as a sandwich filling between two slices of bread...

Q8 **Rewrite** the sentences below, **joining** the **points** correctly with the **best words** from the box:

as a result of	however	as soon as	until

Point One	**Point Two**
The guest of honour failed to arrive	the experiment going wrong.
The spy waited	the party went ahead as planned.
Joanne booked her flights	the hotel booking was confirmed.
The science lab exploded	the coast was clear.

a) ....

....

b) ....

....

c) ....

....

d) ....

....

Q9 Write down all the **connectives** below in the correct **boxes**:

consequently   however   moreover   later   despite this

furthermore   in spite of this   afterwards   nevertheless   therefore

Words which put an **opposite / different view**:	Words to write about something which **happened because of** the thing you've just written about:

Words to say **more of the same**, or to **back up** what you've just written:	Words to write about something which **happened at a later time**:

52

Paragraphs

I've had an absolute disaster with my paragraphs in these passages — see if you can help...

Q1 Read the passage below about chocolate cake. It's quite hard to read — make things **clearer** by putting in some helpful **paragraph markers** (//):

I once knew a boy who would only eat chocolate cake. He was very particular about what kind of chocolate cake he would eat — cakes with butter icing were okay, but he refused to eat any chocolate cakes with fudge or cherry in them. We first met in Year 7, and I love chocolate, so I knew we would be friends straightaway. However, by the time we were in Year 9, I started to find him really annoying. I had grown sick of the smell of chocolate, and sick of the sight of him. Nowadays I live in a different town, so I rarely see him. I often wonder whether or not he still only eats chocolate cake.

Q2 I've forgotten to use **paragraphs** in this passage.
See if you can help me out with some **double strikes** (//):

My great grandmother is just about to turn one hundred. She is an amazing woman who's still really active, despite her age; but she is also very difficult to please. Last year, to celebrate her ninety-ninth birthday, my whole family stayed at the King Richard Hotel. We had a big, expensive dinner, and then stayed the night so that no one would have to drive. Everyone had a great time, except my great grandmother, who complained that the jelly wasn't wobbly enough, and the ice cream was too icy. We're going to Paris for her hundredth birthday, which is an amazing birthday treat. I don't think she can possibly find anything to complain about in the beautiful French capital. I've just remembered — she hates flying, so maybe Paris isn't the best idea after all.

Q3 Oh dear, I've forgotten to use **paragraphs**... again.
Try to **break up** this passage using **double strikes** (//):

In the 19th century, women did not have the same rights as men. One of the main differences was that women did not have the right to vote. This resulted in a campaign for women's suffrage (the right to vote). There were two main groups of protesters — the Suffragists and the Suffragettes. The Suffragists focused on peaceful protests, whilst the Suffragettes were more violent. They burned down churches, chained themselves to railings and sometimes even attacked politicians. Emmeline Pankhurst was perhaps the most famous campaigner, and she was renowned for her courage. Sadly, Pankhurst died in June 1928, just weeks before all women over 21 were given the right to vote. The Suffragette movement was extremely important in British politics, although many people still believe that there are not enough women in politics today.

Paragraphs

Paragraphs just love a piece of the action — they jump right in and split things up.

Q4 Rewrite the **passage** below, adding **paragraphs** in the correct places:

The Swamp Martians live in a quagmire on the top of Misty Moor. It is a lonely, boggy place, full of foul smells and strange creatures. Mrs Waterweed, head of the Swamp Martian clan, tries her best to make life in the quagmire comfortable, whether it means filling the house with flowers, or cooking her famous eel and marsh gas soup — an activity she was currently engaged in. Over in a neighbouring bog, her husband, Mr Waterweed, was fishing for eels. Whilst fishing, he kept an eye out for 'Gobbling Goo' — a type of mud which could suck him up if he wasn't careful. "Dinner's ready," Mrs Waterweed suddenly cried. An hour later, both the Waterweeds sat back in their chairs feeling happy and well-fed.

....

....

....

....

....

....

....

....

....

....

....

....

....

....

....

....

Q5 Write down the **reasons** why you started each paragraph in **Q4**:

I started the second paragraph because ....

I started the third paragraph because ....

I started the fourth paragraph because ....

I started the fifth paragraph because ....

Negatives

Life is full of dos, but it's also full of don'ts. That's why we need negatives.
I'm quite positive about using negatives — that's why I'm giving you these questions...

Q1   Rewrite the sentences below so that the **negatives** are correct:

a)   You've got no chance of not winning.

....

b)   The aliens can't find nowhere to land.

....

c)   Barry doesn't think no one will come.

....

d)   The lads don't have nothing to be afraid of.

....

e)   Ivan has three sweets, but Drew don't have none.

....

f)   Arthur and Merlin doesn't need no help.

....

Q2   Rewrite the sentences below, replacing '**ain't**' with the correct **long forms**:

a)   Abdul wants some sweets, but Gillian *ain't* got any.

....

b)   I *ain't* got anything to lose.

....

c)   Tom wants a day off, but that *ain't* going to happen.

....

d)   I *ain't* dyeing my hair green and Charlie *ain't* shaving his beard off.

....

....

e)   The Johnsons *ain't* got any pets.

....

f)   Irene *ain't* finished her work yet.

....

Mixed Questions

A mixed bag of questions is coming up. This page looks at word types.
Language is made up of lots of different word types — I bet you're dying of suspense...

Q1 Match the following **definitions** with the **correct words** from the box:

noun	adjective	verb	article	preposition
main clause		subordinate clause		adverb

a) word that tells you what something is doing or being ....

b) clause which can stand by itself and make sense ....

c) word which describes a verb ....

d) word used for naming a person, place or thing ....

e) describing word which tells you more about a noun ....

f) clause which doesn't make sense on its own ....

g) word that introduces a phrase about time or place ....

h) word that introduces a noun ....

Q2 Write down two different **examples** of each word type listed from the passage below:

Yesterday we went for a jolly trip on a boat. It was an absolutely gorgeous day, so we didn't pack anything. We had supplies on the boat to make snacks for everyone as we went along the narrow canal.

verbs: ....   common nouns: ....

....

articles: ....   prepositions: ....

....

adverbs: ....   adjectives: ....

....

Q3 Change each of these **verbs** into **nouns** by adding either '**-ence**' or '**-tion**':

a) interfere ....   e) participate ....

b) exist ....   f) complicate ....

c) dedicate ....   g) elevate ....

d) persist ....   h) refer ....

56

Mixed Questions

You can never have too many mixed questions, as I always say — so here are some more...

Q4 Tick the options below which are necessary **features of all sentences**:

a) A verb ☐

b) A preposition ☐

c) A subject ☐

d) It contains a complete idea ☐

e) Punctuation ☐

f) An object ☐

g) At least one capital letter ☐

h) It needs to be a statement ☐

i) At least four words ☐

j) At least two clauses ☐

Q5 Use the **clauses** and **connectives** below to make up **six complex sentences**. You can only use each clause or connective **once**. Add your own **prepositional phrase** to each sentence to give it more detail. The first one has been done for you:

First Clause	Connectives	Second Clause
Sally didn't see the mess	wherever	he couldn't drive to work.
I hate the feel of toothpaste	and hence	it had eaten too many biscuits.
Mike forgot to get some petrol	even though	they go.
The cat couldn't eat its tea	until	she stepped in it.
Phil and Ben kept smiling	whereas	they were having a bad day.
United fans always sing loudly	because	I love the feel of mouthwash.

a) *Sally didn't see the mess on the floor until she stepped in it.*

b)

c)

d)

e)

f)

Section Three — Grammar: Basics

Mixed Questions

You've reached the last page of questions for this section. Give yourself a big pat on the back. Just two more questions to go and then it's full steam ahead to Section Four...

Q6 Fill in the gaps below with either **'don't'** or **'doesn't'**:

a) Ulrich .... know me, and Karl .... know me either.

b) You .... own a car, and Riony .... own a bike.

c) Stuart and Elaine .... have a cat, and we .... have a dog.

d) Lillian .... want to come shopping, but I .... like shopping on my own.

Q7 Rewrite the passage below, **correcting** all of the **mistakes**:

On wednesday Malcolm are celebrating her sixteenth birthday, so he and me are going to the cinema. We thought about inviting Emily, therefore she's going on holiday to france that day and can't come. However, I'm sure we'll have a great time anyway. I've already bought his present, who is going to be a big surprise. It's a navy, blue football, shirt, with the number three in the back — that's his lucky number. He ain't a big football fan, but when he was talking to Liam, whose mad about the sport, Malcolm said he'd like a football shirt. I can't wait to see him open his present — he's not going to have no idea what it is.

....

....

....

....

....

....

....

....

....

....

....

....

....

....

Section Four — Grammar: Tenses

Writing About Now

Forget about yesterday. Don't think about tomorrow. Let's focus on what's happening now...

Q1 Circle the correct present tense **verb agreements** below:

a) He *say / says*   **d)** They *make / makes*   **g)** It *seem / seems*

b) I *know / knows*   **e)** She *take / takes*   **h)** We *show / shows*

c) We *play / plays*   **f)** You *complain / complains*   **i)** I *tell / tells*

Q2 Rewrite these sentences with the correct **present tense** form of the verbs in brackets:

a) Stanley *(to fly)* to New York every year.

....

b) Ron *(to catch)* the bus to work.

....

c) Our grandpa *(to go)* to night school.

....

d) Houri *(to pass)* the ball to Greg.

....

e) Ann *(to fry)* the bacon in the morning.

....

f) Clive *(to do)* his exercises every day.

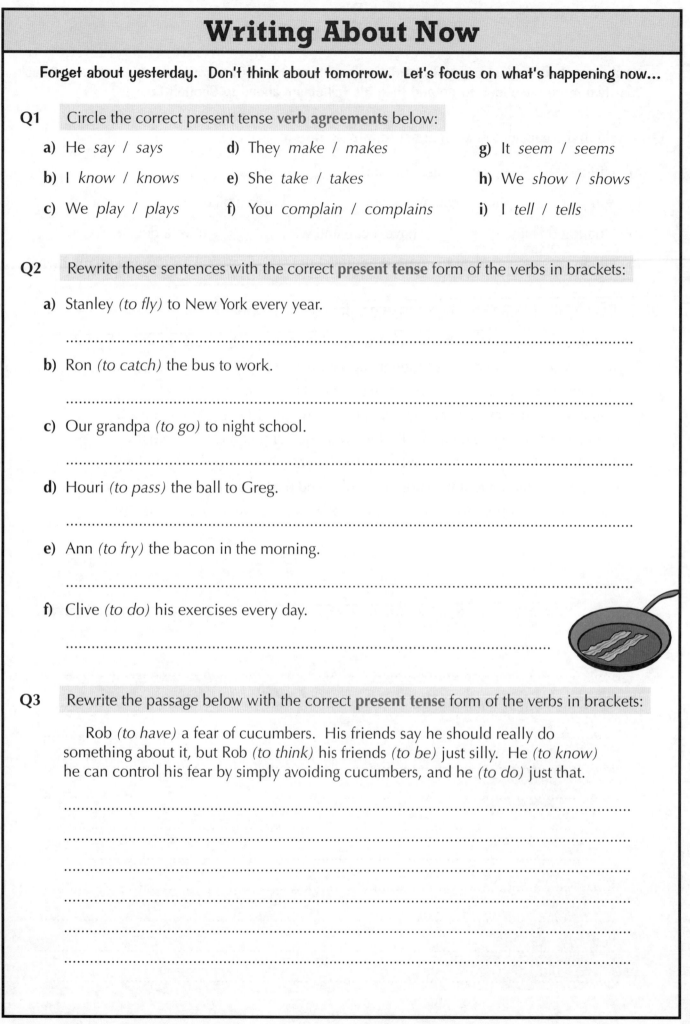

....

Q3 Rewrite the passage below with the correct **present tense** form of the verbs in brackets:

Rob *(to have)* a fear of cucumbers. His friends say he should really do something about it, but Rob *(to think)* his friends *(to be)* just silly. He *(to know)* he can control his fear by simply avoiding cucumbers, and he *(to do)* just that.

....

....

....

....

....

....

Writing About Now

I'm psychic and I can prove it — I bet that right now you're reading this sentence...

Q4 Complete the tables below using the **present tense** with '**-ing**':

Present Tense	'-ing Form'	Present Tense	'-ing Form'
He talks	....	They sleep	....
They help	....	It rains	....
I ask	....	We keep	....
It melts	....	I eat	....

Q5 Rewrite the passage below with the correct **present tense** with '**-ing**' form of the verbs in brackets:

The annual Galaxy Gala is in full swing, but it's all *(to go)* wrong. The balloons *(to pop)*, the waiters *(to drop)* the dishes, a Venus Vole *(to dig)* holes in the floor, and dangerous Mars Mutants *(to tap)* at the door to be let in. The guests are not happy and the organiser *(to offer)* everyone refunds.

....

....

....

....

....

....

....

Q6 Rewrite the sentences below in the **present tense** with '**-ing**':

a) The scouts tie knots in their leader's shoelaces.

....

b) Cassie battles to keep her eyes open.

....

c) Jaden and Terese dye their hair.

....

Writing About the Past

This page lets us write about yesterday, last week, last month and even last year...

Q1 Complete the tables below with the correct **simple past tense** forms of the verbs:

Verbs	The Simple Past
talk	....
hope	....
doubt	....
ask	....
work	....

Verbs	The Simple Past
tease	....
offer	....
practise	....
play	....
behave	....

Q2 Rewrite the verbs below in their **simple past tense** forms:

a) I give: ➡ ....

b) He is: ➡ ....

c) We take: ➡ ....

d) They sleep: ➡ ....

e) It travels: ➡ ....

f) She keeps: ➡ ....

g) You tell: ➡ ....

h) We spill: ➡ ....

i) I copy: ➡ ....

j) They build: ➡ ....

k) You see: ➡ ....

l) He grows: ➡ ....

m) It sweeps: ➡ ....

n) She hears: ➡ ....

Q3 Rewrite the passage below so that the **simple past tense** is used **correctly**:

Yesterday we maked a birthday card for Granny. We cutted shapes out of paper and sticked them onto some card. Dad buyed her a present and Mum hided it behind the sofa. They wroted clues for Granny to follow, and she quickly founded the present.

....

....

....

....

....

Section Four — Grammar: Tenses

The Past Tense with Have

History teachers will just love this page — like the last one, this is about the past too...

Q1 Complete the tables below with the correct **past tense with 'have'** forms of the verbs:

Verbs	Past with 'have'
She eats	....
It is	....
They go	....
I arrive	....
We give	....

Verbs	Past with 'have'
He finishes	....
You write	....
We have	....
It takes	....
I show	....

Q2 Rewrite the sentences below so that the **past tense with 'have'** is used **correctly**:

a) I been to see the doctor.

....

b) We done a great job.

....

c) They not done the washing-up.

....

d) Caleb seen the new Jenny Pond film.

....

e) I have did my best.

....

f) We been living here for ages.

....

Q3 Circle the correct word in **italics** in each of these sentences so that they make sense:

a) Jeff knows *have* / *of* a nice café.

b) They should *have* / *of* been in bed.

c) I could *have* / *of* been a film star.

d) Mel might *have* / *of* joined in.

e) I thought *have* / *of* a possible plan.

f) She should *have* / *of* known better.

Staying in the Right Tense

Some things are meant to change, like the guards at Buckingham Palace, but other things are better off staying just as they are, like the tenses you use in your work.

Q1 Write out these sentences, **making changes** to the **tense** of the **verb** where necessary:

a) On Tuesday we had a buffet and we have played board games.

....

b) Yesterday the superhero saves the President and rescues his cat.

....

c) I am keen to learn Spanish and had decided to take lessons.

....

d) My printer had broken and so I need to go shopping.

....

e) The sales are on, so I go to the shops right now.

....

Q2 The tenses in the passage below **aren't consistent**. Rewrite it with the **correct tenses**:

Last Saturday, Hootle Village Hall is holding its annual autumn fair. There is a car boot sale, which is offering clothes and toys; there was a cake stall, which has sold a selection of bakery items; and there has been a face-painting stand. A raffle will also take place, and for the children there is going to be a line-dancing competition. The mayor is also coming, and he helps to run some of the stands. The fair was raising over £300 for the local community.

....
....
....
....
....
....
....
....
....

Mixed Questions

Don't let this page make you feel tense, just because it has some questions on tenses...

Q1 Rewrite these sentences by putting them into the **present tense**:

a) I was in Spain for my holiday.

....

b) We played catch with the neighbours.

....

c) I walked from the church to the circus.

....

d) I didn't know what he was.

....

Q2 Put each of the sentences below into the **past tense**:

a) The spy speaks five languages.

....

b) They only buy meat from the butcher's.

....

c) I am on the school's netball team, and I play squash.

....

d) Kelsey listens to the radio and whistles along.

....

Q3 Rewrite each of the sentences below in the **tense** shown in **brackets**:

a) Harvey thinks a lot about taking over the world. *(simple past)*

....

b) Samia passed her exam with flying colours. *(past tense with 'have')*

....

c) Norris and his horse have won the race. *(present tense '-ing' form)*

....

d) Stella will take her sister to ballet lessons. *(present tense)*

....

Mixed Questions

Mixed questions are here to keep you on your toes — you never know what might crop up...

Q4 Complete the table below with the correct **verb forms**:

Present Tense	Present '-ing' Form	Simple Past	Past Tense with 'have'
He goes	....	....	....
....	....	....	We have seen
....	They are taking	....	....
....	....	I began	....

Q5 There are some mistakes in the tenses in the passage below.
Rewrite the passage **correctly** underneath:

Last week, the headmaster at Piggleswick High School will turn his school into a giant jungle gym for a day. He replaces the stairs with inflatable slides and put a bouncy castle in the hall. To get out of the staff room, the teachers are having to use a fireman's pole. The headmaster is also building a fort out of plastic bricks in the dining room. All the pupils are thinking it was a great idea.

Today, it's the pupils' turn to decorate the school. Right now, they is blowing up balloons and hung streamers in the classrooms. The head girl are making party hats while the prefects have baked food for a buffet.

....
....
....
....
....
....
....
....
....
....
....
....
....

Writing in Standard English

Standard English can be pretty confusing, but it's super important that you use it in most of your written work. These questions should help you get it sorted in your head...

Q1 Read the statements below and write 'true' or 'false' on the dotted lines:

a) You should avoid using double negatives in Standard English. ....

b) Non-Standard English is usually found in spoken rather than written English. ....

c) Verbs and subjects should agree in Standard English (e.g. 'We were late' instead of 'We was late'). ....

d) Television soaps provide a good example of correct spoken Standard English. ....

e) You can use non-Standard English in your work for some creative writing. ....

f) Using non-Standard English makes your writing clear and easy to understand. ....

Q2 **Match** each **non-Standard English** phrase with a **Standard English** equivalent:

I were right	going to	I was correct
ain't		
gonna	I saw him	that is implausible
I done it		
not likely	am not / is not etc.	
		I did it
I seen him		

Q3 Tick the boxes next to the situations where you should use **Standard English**:

a) Writing to apply to be an astronaut ☐

b) Shouting to a friend to pass you the ball ☐

c) Showing parents around your school ☐

d) Writing a letter to the Prime Minister ☐

e) Giving a tourist directions ☐

f) Arguing over what to watch at your friend's house ☐

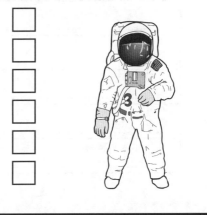

66

Writing in Standard English

This is another pretty standard page — it's on Standard English... I crack myself up.

Q4   **Rewrite** the sentences below in **Standard English:**

a)   I done real well — I think I done better than last time.

....

b)   The man what came yesterday were well strange.

....

c)   We was waiting for like ages, but we ain't never seen him.

....

d)   I asked him for a lend of his pen and he give it me.

....

e)   It don't have to be like this — we ain't got to argue.

....

f)   I never did nothing — it weren't me what broke it.

....

Q5   **Sort** these phrases into **Standard English** and **non-Standard English** and write them in the tables below:

a)   He is well good at chess.

b)   This is a real example.

c)   I'd like them biscuits.

d)   I have wrote them a letter.

e)   We never knew why.

f)   This is not proper behaviour.

g)   The essay is well written.

h)   I should of known better.

i)   I was proper glad.

j)   There were none left.

Standard English	Non-Standard English
....	....
....	....
....	....
....	....
....	....

Writing in Standard English

Yep, that's right — more on Standard English. But bear with me — you're very nearly done...

Q6 Underline the correct option from the words in **italics**, so that each sentence uses **Standard English**:

a) *They goes / They go* out all the time.

b) *I did / I done* it right the first time.

c) I don't know if *they is / they are* here.

d) I thought *he were / he was* coming.

e) *That was / That were* terrifying.

f) *I have been / I been* away.

g) They *have given / have gave* us gifts.

h) *It was / It were* the best party ever.

Q7 **Rewrite** the article below in correct **Standard English**:

When we was children, people wasn't allowed to waste anything. We made everything go a right long way. Our mum would scold us for throwing away anything what might still be useful. She would watch us to make sure we had ate everything what she gave us. Rationing meant you had to be real inventive with the cooking. Yet no one ever said they didn't like nothing, not even our Alice.

In them days we didn't have no modern vacuum cleaners and washing machines, like. We wouldn't of had money for nothing like that. But you wouldn't never have heard no one complaining. I ain't never known nothing like it since.

....

....

....

....

....

....

....

....

....

....

....

....

Writing in the Right Style

Getting your style right is essential if you want to give the right impression in your writing...

Q1 Look at the list of **text types** below and **sort** each one into the correct box:

a) politician's speech

b) e-mail to a friend

c) job application

d) school science report

e) text message to a friend

f) postcard to your cousin

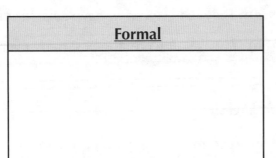

Formal	**Informal**

Q2 Look at the **text types** below. For each one choose the **most appropriate formality** from the options in the box and write it on the dotted lines:

> very formal   quite formal   fairly informal   very informal

a) A letter of apology to your head teacher   ....

b) An advert for an anti-spot cream for teenage magazine readers   ....

c) A text message about a football match to your best mate   ....

d) A book report to be read aloud to your friends in class   ....

Q3 Draw lines to **match** each **informal** expression with an appropriate **formal** version:

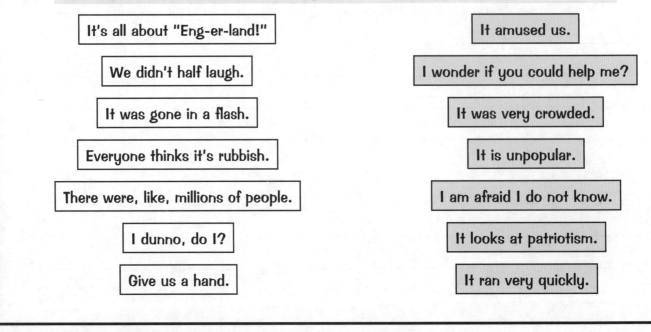

It's all about "Eng-er-land!"

We didn't half laugh.

It was gone in a flash.

Everyone thinks it's rubbish.

There were, like, millions of people.

I dunno, do I?

Give us a hand.

It amused us.

I wonder if you could help me?

It was very crowded.

It is unpopular.

I am afraid I do not know.

It looks at patriotism.

It ran very quickly.

Section Five — Writing Skills

Writing in the Right Style

Choosing a formal or informal style can be tricky — think about who your audience is...

Q4 Write down whether each of the following sentences is **formal** or **informal**:

a) I wish to make a complaint about the quality
of service in this establishment. ....

b) Please keep the noise down and show some respect. ....

c) Shut it, will you? Can't you see I'm trying to sleep? ....

d) I'm getting kind of fed up with the waitress ignoring me. ....

e) That striker played a blinder today; he's worth every penny. ....

f) The footballer showed incredible dexterity on
the pitch; he deserves to be well paid for his services. ....

Q5 Underline the **informal words** in the sentences below:

a) The England manager said he was gutted about their defeat.

b) It looks like it will rain cats and dogs on Saturday.

c) The ladies yakked to each other on the phone for an hour.

d) When Duncan asked for the day off, his boss told him to get lost.

e) Mrs Gladding's dishwasher had conked out, so she called the plumber.

f) The film tracks his relationship with his girlfriend, and ends when she dumps him.

Q6 Using the words in the box below, fill in the **gaps** in the letter in a **suitable style**:

tasteless / gross	an appalling / a lousy	rude / impolite	inform / tell
hearing from you asap / your response		I'm / I am	try / endeavour

Dear Mr Spudwrangler,

.... writing to .... you that I recently had

.... meal at one of your Spudwrangler restaurants. The waiters

were ...., and the food was ....

I hope that you will .... to make things right.

I look forward to ....

Yours sincerely,
Toby Brown

Writing in the Right Style

I know what you're thinking — 'Right now I really fancy a page of questions on style...'

Q7   **Rewrite** the sentences below in a more **formal** style:

a)   He said it was a pile of pants.

....

b)   Chuck us a packet of crisps — ta, mate.

....

c)   Your mam's going to play merry hell with you for the state of your shoes.

....

....

d)   The criminal said he'd not nicked the motor nor anything else.

....

....

e)   This Vincent van Gogh geezer was a big-name artist that got so fed up,
he went and sliced his own ear off.

....

....

f)   When Shakespeare was about, people got ill pretty much all the time
and bags of people had the plague.

....

....

Q8   **Rewrite** the passage below in a more **informal** style:

I am writing to inform the family that I am having an excellent holiday with my friends. I have done a lot of sunbathing; and in addition to this I have been engaging in various cultural activities. It is a shame that you were unable to come with me. I sincerely hope that you are well and I look forward to seeing you soon.

....

....

....

....

....

....

Writing in the Right Style

Getting your writing style wrong is like turning up to prom in your tracksuit — super awkward.
Make sure you've got the style memo with these last few questions...

Q9 Read the **informal** description below and **rewrite** it in the style of an encyclopedia entry:

The Shetland Islands are a group of islands just up from, and a bit right of, the Orkneys. In the 9th century, some Vikings sneaked in and took over the islands. Those Norse types held on to the islands for ages until eventually, in 1471, Scotland grabbed control of them. The Shetland Islands' history means their culture is a bit of a mash-up of Norse and Scottish traditions.

Most of the Shetland Islands' money comes from lots of fishing, but the islands are also famous for those cute little Shetland Ponies.

....

....

....

....

....

....

....

....

....

....

Q10 **Underline** the more **formal** sentence in each pair below, and then use the dotted lines to write down why you think your underlined sentences seem **more formal** than the others:

a) The statue was unveiled by the mayor.
The mayor unveiled the statue.

Hint: Look at the type of voice the different sentences use.

b) Residents were shocked by the decision to close the library.
The closure of the library shocked the residents.

c) Local artists were commissioned by the council.
The council commissioned local artists.

....

....

....

Choosing Active or Passive

Stand up and do star jumps for active sentences. Sit back and relax for the passive ones...

Q1 Pair up the **active sentences** below with the matching **passive sentences**:

Mum put the clocks back.	The trees were felled.
The postman took the letters to Santa.	My car was repaired.
Mike fixed my car.	The wood was set alight.
The men tidied the church.	The clocks were changed.
Lydia set fire to the wood.	The letters were delivered to Santa.
They cut the trees down.	The church was cleaned.

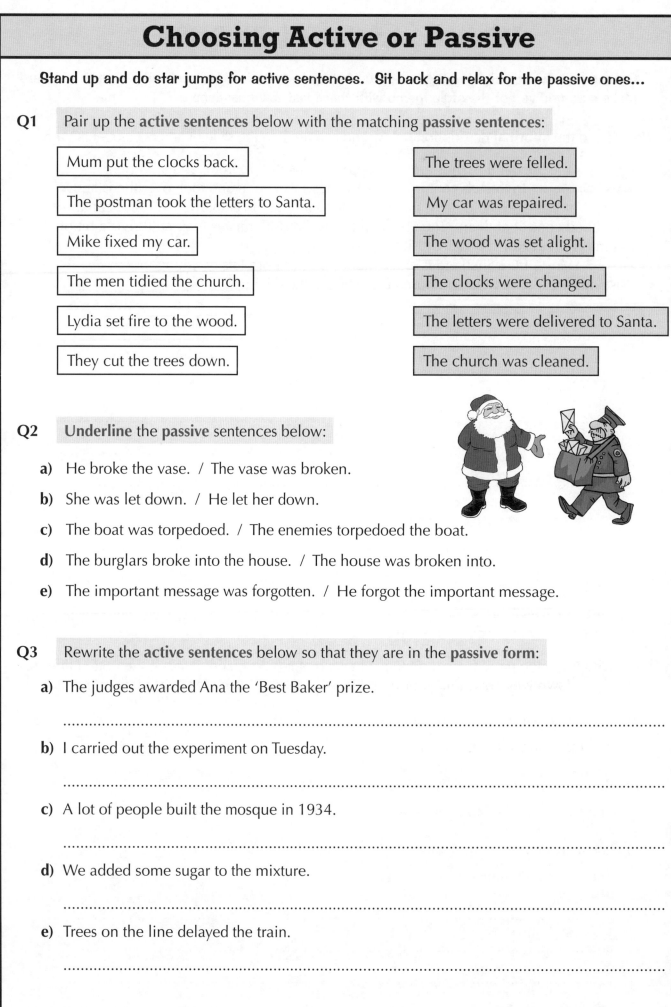

Q2 **Underline** the **passive** sentences below:

a) He broke the vase. / The vase was broken.

b) She was let down. / He let her down.

c) The boat was torpedoed. / The enemies torpedoed the boat.

d) The burglars broke into the house. / The house was broken into.

e) The important message was forgotten. / He forgot the important message.

Q3 Rewrite the **active sentences** below so that they are in the **passive form**:

a) The judges awarded Ana the 'Best Baker' prize.

....

b) I carried out the experiment on Tuesday.

....

c) A lot of people built the mosque in 1934.

....

d) We added some sugar to the mixture.

....

e) Trees on the line delayed the train.

....

Choosing Active or Passive

I tried to tell my granny about the passive, but she just passed me a sieve...

Q4   Rewrite the **passive** sentences below so that they are in the **active form**:

a)   This subject was already discussed by us.

   ....

b)   A new system was introduced by them.

   ....

c)   The school was visited by several famous people.

   ....

d)   The whole house was cleaned by the servants.

   ....

e)   She was admired by him.

   ....

f)   Their hair was washed and their faces were scrubbed by me.

   ....

Q5   Look at the reasons below. Write down whether each one
   could be a **reason** for **using** an **active** or **passive sentence**:

a)   When it is not important to say who did something.   ....

b)   When you want to focus on who did something.   ....

c)   When you want your writing to be clear and easy to read.   ....

d)   When you want to create suspense.   ....

e)   When you want a bossy or serious tone.   ....

Q6   Circle the **subjects** in the sentences below:

a)   Ian held the racquets.

b)   Ishram was seen by the guard.

c)   The competitors were warned by the referee.

d)   Marianne ordered a kebab.

Spelling Tips

Spelling is downright tricky. I wonder if there's a mnemonic for the word 'mnemonic'...

Q1 Write down your own **mnemonics** for the following words:

a) rhythm

....

....

Mnemonics are sentences or phrases that can help you remember spellings. E.g. Because — Big Elephants Can Always Understand Small Elephants.

b) necessary

....

....

c) immediately

....

....

Q2 Write down how you might **break up** the following words:

a) development ....

b) furthermore ....

c) embarrassing ....

d) accommodation ....

e) relative ....

f) international ....

g) unfashionably ....

h) unfortunately ....

Tip: There's no right or wrong answers here. Do what works best to help you remember how to spell the words.

Q3 Put the words below into **three** groups. The words in each group should all share a **letter combination**:

antique	guest	nought	banquet	fatigue	tongue
drought	quality	tough	guitar	queen	thorough

....

....

....

....

Spelling Tips

This page smells a bit sweaty — it's full of memory-joggers. These are handy letters which remind us how to spell words. Hopefully they won't run away...

Q4 Work out the **answers** to the **clues** below and then find the words in the word search:

a) If you go on holiday, you'll need to book this. (13)

b) You usually write this on an envelope. (7)

c) Another word for vanish. (9)

d) This person lives next door. (9)

e) The day before Thursday. (9)

```
Y X W N I E G H B U R A A
V U T O S R Q P O A D R C
N M L I K J I H G D F U C
W E N S D A Y E R R D O O
Y L A A B A Z E Y E X B M
A D Y D W V S U T S R H M
D I B O Q S P D N S M G O
S S O M R A E P P A S I D
E A U M L K J I H G N E A
N P R O R U B H G I E N T
D E F C D I S A P E A R I
E E E C Y A D S D N E W O
W R C A D R R E S S B A N
```

Q5 Add the correct word from the box to each **sentence below**:

Emma	rat	gain	lie	secret

a) There's a .... in separate.

b) There's a .... in belief.

c) You .... when you get a bargain.

d) The secretary has a ....

e) .... faced a dilemma.

Q6 In each sentence in **Q5** underline the **letters** which act as a **memory-jogger**:

Q7 Write down **three words** which you find **difficult** to spell. For each of these words write down a **short sentence** which acts as a **memory-jogger**:

1) ....
....

2) ....
....

3) ....
....

Section Five — Writing Skills

76

Mixed Questions

Behold this page of mixed questions and admire its mixed-up glory. It's the last one — yippee!

Q1 Rewrite the sentences below using **Standard English**:

a) They ain't got no choice.

....

b) Me and Harvey is giving it our best shot.

....

c) I'm well mad about them robberies.

....

Q2 Rewrite these sentences using **formal English**:

a) Neville nicked fifty quid. ⇨ ....

b) That would've cost a bomb. ⇨ ....

Q3 Complete the table below with **active sentences** and **passive sentences**:

Active Sentence	Passive Sentence
Anna wrote the poem.	....
....	He was seen by you.
A little elf bit me.	....
....	We were caught by the teacher.

Q4 Rewrite the passage below, changing any **passive sentences** into **active sentences**:

Yesterday the pupils at Blackhaven School were treated to a party by the teachers. A band was booked by the secretary, and guests were invited to attend by the headmistress. Fizzy pop was banned by the janitor, but the pupils were encouraged to bring their own food by the deputy head.

....

....

....

....

....

Section Five — Writing Skills

EGW31